Turbine - and Jet - propelled
AIRCRAFT POWERPLANTS

by

JAMES P. EAMES

Major, United States Air Force
Consulting Aeronautical and Mechanical Engineer

1954

CHARTWELL HOUSE, INC.

280 Madison Avenue   New York, New York

FOREWORD

Jet and turbine propulsion represent the newest of advancements in the highly progressive field of aeronautics. While at the present time necessarily and almost wholly monopolized by the tactical requirements of military aviation, this lusty infant is already spreading exploratory fingers into the realm of commercial air transport, and even into the exclusive domain of the private and sportsman flyer.

The vast and still somewhat mysterious scope of nuclear energy, on whose doorstep we now stand expectantly, offers a great, untapped potential for aircraft propulsion power. Here, again, nuclear aircraft powerplants, when they actually become a reality, should align themselves with, and even faithfully resemble, contemporary jet units, both in principle and in configuration.

It behooves those of us who have spawned the reciprocating engine and have proudly nurtured it through two decades of truly phenomenal development, to again prepare to unleash a reservoir of power of practically undreamed of potential, even when gauged by the standards of the extremely fruitful wartime years.

This volume should effectively bridge the ever-widening gap between the jet engine and the reliable old reciprocator, with its exasperating repertoire of vexing problems, long since solved by men who themselves, two decades ago, initiated the grasp of those problems even as our new crop of engineers, technicians, and mechanics are doing today with the many intriguing facets of reactive propulsion design and operation. It is my hope that this volume will set many of these neophytes on the road to knowledge and subsequent achievement.

The author, Major James P. Eames, has spent the greater part of his life in the thunderous and fast-moving environment of aircraft powerplants. It is fitting that he should contribute this volume which is so timely and of such interest.

The text is remarkable in that it is sufficiently and authoritatively technical to absorb the interest of the practicing engineer, and yet is so simply and plainly written that it can be useful to the aviation student and tyro technician.

Harry P. Christofferson

"Early Birds"

PREFACE

The impact of turbine and jet propulsion in the field of aircraft powerplants is such that it can no longer be ignored. Already, the large airline carriers are showing great interest in these attractive methods of aircraft propulsion. The armed services are in the advanced-planning stages of an all-jet, all-turbine air force structure.

Almost daily, we hear of new developments aimed at reducing the overhead costs and, at the same time, increasing the operating efficiency of aircraft turbine powerplants which will be ultimately unanimously accepted.

The huge task of introducing workable jet and turbine aircraft engines has been accomplished by farseeing technicians, but there are still a great many problems attending large-scale adoption. This volume has been written to assist in the preparation and training of the host of technicians that will be urgently needed when aviation becomes completely turbine conscious.

This book should reach and benefit aviation students; airline technicians and mechanics; military air personnel, including pilots, flight engineers and mechanics; engineering and aviation students, at both the university and vocational trade school levels. Reciprocating-engine personnel, who now stand at the threshold of transition to the jet and turbine era, should find much of interest and value in this text. Those who have a cultural interest in the march of science and who will, in the very near future, make extensive use of jet-powered airliners can increase their store of knowledge by perusal of the pages to follow.

CONTENTS

ACKNOWLEDGEMENTS

The author extends his grateful acknowledgement to the following services, corporations, engineering and aviation trade journals, and periodicals for their courtesy and invaluable assistance in making available data and illustrations:

United States Air Force

Bureau of Aeronautics, United States Navy

Aerojet Engineering Corporation

Aviation Age

Aviation Week

Flight

General Electric Company

General Motors, Allison Division

Pratt and Whitney Division, United Aircraft Corporation

Reaction Motors, Incorporated

Timken Roller Bearing Company

Westinghouse Manufacturing Company

Wright Aeronautical Corporation

Chapter 1

INTRODUCTION

Basic Principles of Reactive Propulsion

The basic principle of jet propulsion is neither new nor particularly complicated. It is, in effect, the identical elementary force which imparts the energy to a toy balloon when it eludes one's fingers and flies off while deflating through its open neck. It is again manifested in the reactive force that tends to make a firearm "kick" against the rifleman's shoulder. It is, also, the effort that forces a lawn sprinkler to rotate, or that by which a rower forces his craft to move in a direction opposite to the effort of his oars. In fact, a dozen forms of simple jet propulsion may be observed daily, all of them emanating from, and being governed by, the elementary second and third laws of motion, first established by Sir Isaac Newton in 1680. These basic laws state: (2) "The resultant force acting on a body is equal to the product of the mass times the acceleration of the body." (3) "For every action there exists an equal and opposite reaction."

Newton's second law of motion is expressed as follows:

$$F = Kma \qquad (1)$$

where F = resultant force K = a constant, the values of which depends on the units m = mass of the body and
a = acceleration or rate of change of velocity.

1

This equation may also be expressed as follows:

$$F = \frac{W}{g} a \qquad (2)$$

where F and a have the same meaning as before and K is assumed to equal unity

W = weight of the body in pounds and g = acceleration of gravity (32.2 ft/sec/sec).

$$F = \frac{W (V_2 - V_1)}{g \quad t} \qquad (3)$$

where V_2 = final velocity (ft/sec), V_1 = initial velocity (ft/sec), and

t = time of the action (sec).

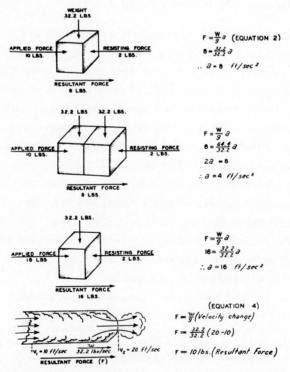

FIGURE 1. Illustrations of Newton's Second Law of Motion.

$$F = \frac{w}{g} \quad \text{(velocity change)} \quad (4)$$

where w = rate of flow (lb/sec).

Figure 1 illustrates various applications of Newton's second law of motion. Figure 2 is an illustration of Newton's third law of motion.

Quite rightly, then, the principle of jet propulsion can be termed "reactive propulsion." In jet-propelled aircraft, hot combustion gases are generated and permitted to expand by one of several methods which will be discussed in detail later in this book. These gases are then ejected into the atmosphere through a restricted orifice located at, or near, the rear of the aircraft. The impelling force, which imparts forward motion to the aircraft, originates from the reaction caused by the rapid exit of the fluid stream from the jet orifice, and is internally impressed on the structure of the jet powerplant. Contrary to popular conception, the motion of the aircraft is not the result of the push exerted by the jetted gases on the mass of atmospheric air in the wake of the aircraft. This fact can be more readily understood when it is

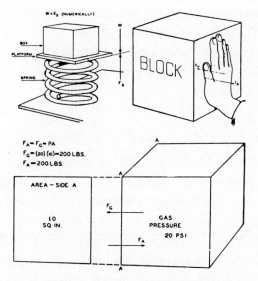

FIGURE 2. Illustrations of Newton's Third Law of Motion.

considered that the reactive force is developed irrespective of the nature or the density of the surrounding medium.

COMPUTATION OF THRUST FORCE

The power output of jet-propelled aircraft powerplants is measured and given in thrust units, rather than in the standard horsepower rating employed in connection with the conventional reciprocating engine. Thrust can be interpreted as the reactive force exerted, in pounds of pressure, by the heated air and combustion gases directly on the aircraft in order to propel it forward. Actually, the jet-propelled aircraft powerplant attains its thrust by changing the momentum, or the product obtained when the mass of air utilized is multiplied by the change in velocity to which this air mass is subjected. In other words, the thrust force can be considered as equal to the mass of the jet discharge per second multiplied by the jet velocity relative to that of the aircraft. It must be considered, however, that the velocity of the jet charge assumes a value of zero prior to flight and that, in the course of acceleration of the aircraft, the fuel charge must also be accelerated. Otherwise, particularly when the flight velocity exceeded the jet velocity, an initial error would be introduced into the calculations.

In order to compute actual values of thrust, we must remember that the gross thrust is equal to the product of the mass of air utilized times the velocity change, or:

$$F = M \times V_e \qquad \text{or}$$

$$F = \frac{W}{g} \times V_e$$

To select a hypothetical example: A certain turbojet powerplant utilizes 85 pounds air per second at 100% rpm and at standard day conditions. The velocity change is assumed to be 1,870 feet per second.

The gross thrust is then:
$$F = \frac{85 \times 1870}{32.2} = 4{,}936 \text{ pounds.}$$

Net thrust is developed when the velocity of the jet exceeds the velocity of the aircraft, i.e., only in motion. As soon as the jet airplane starts to move down the runway we get net thrust. Net thrust is expressed as:

$$N.T. = \frac{W (V_o - V_p)}{g}$$

where W and g have the same meaning as in the previous equation.

V_o is the velocity of the jet (airstream) and

V_p is the velocity of the aircraft.

The net thrust decreases from 0 to 290 miles per hour, since the loss in velocity change is a greater factor than the increase in pounds of air flow. An increase in net thrust beyond 290 miles per hour (true air speed) is the result of the air flow increasing more rapidly than does the loss of velocity change. This trend is readily indicated by the solutions of the following two practical examples, one predicated on an air speed of 290 miles per hour, the other on an air speed of 600 miles per hour.

Let us assume that under standard day conditions and at 290 miles speed per hour, a jet aircraft utilizes a mass of air of 94 pounds per second. The velocity of the jet is 1,900 feet per second. Net thrust will equal:

$$N.T. = \frac{94 (1900 - 425)}{32.2} = 4,330 \text{ pounds} \quad (290 \text{ mph} = 425 \text{ ft/sec})$$

Now let us assume that a jet aircraft flying at 600 miles per hour under standard day conditions utilizes an air mass of 120 pounds per second, and that the velocity change is now 2,200 feet per second. The net thrust then becomes:

$$N.T. = \frac{120 (2200 - 880)}{32.2} = 4,950 \text{ pounds} \quad (600 \text{ mph} = 880 \text{ ft/sec})$$

CONVERSION OF THRUST TO HORSEPOWER UNITS

In order to obtain a proper evaluation of jet powerplant performance by a direct comparison with other conventional prime movers, the reactive thrust force can be readily converted into standard horsepower units. Since jet powerplants are rated on the basis of the number of pounds thrust they can produce at sea level in a static condition, this power output can be converted into horsepower ratings by multiplying true air speed by net thrust and dividing the resulting product by 375. An approximation, adequate for basic computations, can be readily obtained by applying the conversion factor: 1 pound of thrust equals 1 horsepower at 375 miles per hour. Thus, for example, we can assume that a jet powerplant of, say, 5,000 pounds thrust develops 5,000 horsepower at 375 miles per hour. Or, the identical power plant can be said to develop 10,000 horsepower at 750 miles per hour. From these calculations, it might be inferred that the higher the forward velocity attained in the course of operation of the jet powerplant, the greater in direct proportion will be the power developed by the unit.

It is important to understand the basic difference between the true jet-propelled aircraft and the various forms of rocket-propelled craft. Although both types function on the principles of reactive forces, the rocket transports not only its fuel, but also the oxygen content required for complete combustion of the fuel. The true jet-propelled powerplant can be called "air free" because it transports only the basic fuel required for its operation and is forced to absorb the oxygen required for combustion from the atmosphere. In view of this fact, the rocket can ascend to altitudes unattainable by any other existing type of aircraft. The true jet-propelled aircraft, however, has the same limitations which restrict the operation of the conventional reciprocating engine in the thin atmosphere prevalent at extremely high altitudes. However, the rocket craft also has limitations because the high rate of propellant consumption severely restricts its endurance range.

Sonic Speed

The recent powerful stimulus given to jet- and rocket-propelled aircraft design and development is primarily traceable to the search for new media for attaining supersonic speeds, that is, speeds in excess of that of sound. Sonic speed approximates 764 miles per hour at sea level, and 664 miles per hour at an altitude of 40,000 feet above sea level. Velocities of this order have proved generally unattainable by the conventional forms of aircraft because of two outstanding reasons: (1) insufficiency of available power as derived from the conventional reciprocating engine and propeller combination, and (2) the so-called compressibility effect.

As to the first factor, in spite of sweeping developments in the aerodynamic design of propeller-blade sections and many other research accomplishments, the fact remains that the performance limitations imposed by the pronounced reduction in propeller efficiency when tip speeds approach the sonic range preclude employment of the conventional engine-propeller combination for sustained operation beyond the sonic barrier.

COMPRESSIBILITY

The second factor, compressibility, can be designated as the point where a moving object begins to create waves in the fluid medium through which it is passing. Any object moving in a fluid medium is preceded by a compression wave which prepares the fluid for the passage of the object. In the case of a fast-flying, jet-propelled aircraft, this pressure wave will move at about the speed of sound. The mass of atmospheric air contacted by the pressure wave is prepared, so to speak, in such a manner that it will separate and flow about the outer surfaces of the entering aircraft and then recombine smoothly with the atmospheric particles in the wake of the aircraft. However, the velocity of the air flowing over the surfaces of the aircraft varies considerably because it is forced to increase and decrease alternately in order to permit various excrescences and protruding portions of the aircraft to pass. The net result of this situation is that, instead of flowing smoothly about the contour of the aircraft, the atmospheric air is directed against protruding surfaces with high impact force. At the points of impact, alternate bands of compressed and rarefied air are formed. Then, after passing a protruding surface, there is a marked decrease in the velocity of the air particles. These slowed-down particles collide with other air particles moving at, say, sonic velocity from the point which the original particles have just recently occupied. As a direct result, a shock wave, accompanied by high turbulence, is produced at the point of decreased velocity. Additional power is then required to maintain adequate velocity. Control

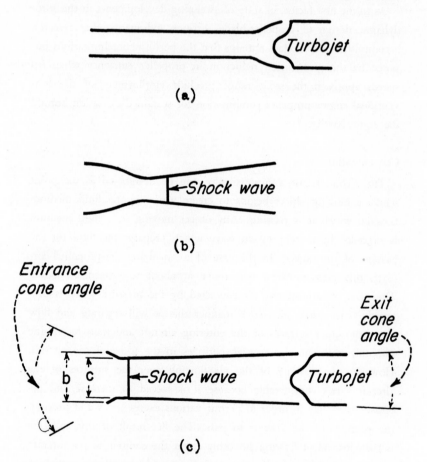

FIGURE 3. *Jet-engine Inlet Ducting:* (a) typical subsonic inlet duct; (b) typical supersonic diffuser; (c) ideal supersonic inlet duct.

of the aircraft is greatly hampered under these conditions, since the shock waves tend to neutralize the control surfaces and to render lift forces negative. From this, it is obvious that an initial requirement for jet-propelled aircraft designed for supersonic performance is high structural strength, in order to withstand the stresses attending the tremendous pressures and the incessant buffeting encountered along an air front of approximately 700 miles per hour.

Jet-engine inlet ducting must be designed to suit the effects of compressibility. This is indicated in figure 3, in which (a) illustrates a typical subsonic inlet duct, (b) is a typical supersonic diffuser, and (c) is an ideal supersonic inlet duct.

It must not be inferred from this discussion that compressibility effects do not appear until the supersonic speed range is attained. Actually, the initial traces of compressibility occur at velocities about one-half that of sound, which is definitely within the subsonic range. A basic reference "yardstick" employed to designate the velocity characteristics of aircraft is the "Mach" number. For example, if the Mach number attained by an aircraft is 0.5, then its performance is evaluated at 50 percent of the velocity of sound. So far, Mach numbers up to 8 have been measured with the aid of wind tunnels of adequate size filled with freon gas.

The Mach number is the ratio of the true air speed of the aircraft to the speed of sound. The speed of sound is solely dependent on temperature, and is independent of barometric pressure. The temperature correction for the speed of sound is given by the equation:

$$ss = 33.5 \sqrt{T_A}$$

where T_A is the absolute temperature, or the observed temperature in °F. plus 460°.

For example, the corrected speed of sound for a temperature of 59°F. is:

$$ss = 33.5 \sqrt{59 + 460} = 33.5 \times 22.78 = 763.18 \text{ miles per hour}$$

The jet-propelled aircraft has proved prominently suitable to overcome compressibility. In the conventional reciprocating engine-propeller combination, the propeller-tip speed and the forward speed of the aircraft represent a velocity combination that rapidly approaches sonic speeds, thus inducing all of the flight disturbances attending compressibility. The forward velocity of the true jet-propelled aircraft, however, is limited only by the tendency of the wings to travel at sonic speed.

Advantages of Jet-propelled Powerplants

The best method of evaluating jet-propelled aircraft is through the comparison of its operation and performance with those of the conventional, propeller-driven aircraft. In the majority of factors, the comparison favors jet aircraft, although certain considerations indicate that the jet-driven aircraft will by no means entirely supplant the conventional airplane for some time to come.

The most prominent advantages of the jet-propelled aircraft are as follows:

(1) Less vibration due to complete absence of reciprocating members. Mechanical vibrators, or "rattlers," are installed on the instrument panels of jet-propelled aircraft in order to insure the functioning of all the instruments, so smooth is the normal operation of these powerplants.

(2) Fewer engine controls and instruments to minimize maintenance and to provide for simpler operation. Minimum pilot attention is needed. One model of a jet-powered medium bomber has a single lever to control power in contrast to the four controls required in the reciprocating engine-propeller combination of a counterpart aircraft. Moreover, the two or more controls for the various air-outlet devices on the latter aircraft are dispensed with on the jet-powered model.

(3) No warm-up period is required. A jet-powered aircraft is ready for flight within 30 seconds after starting. This is a pronounced advantage in tactical "alert" situations. All conventional preflight considerations, such as oil pressure, manifold pressure, etc., are en-

tirely eliminated. The jet units are simply "revved up" in order to check maximum revolutions per minute.

(4) Following the takeoff, it is not necessary to decrease the propeller pitch for normal climb, nor to adjust the mixture control, thus simplifying procedure at this critical time.

(5) The inherent low wing loading and the complete absence of propeller drag contribute to the excellent maneuverability at elevated forward velocities. There are no torque forces for which compensation must be made.

(6) The jet powerplant is highly adaptable to extreme temperature variation. This insures excellent high-altitude operation.

(7) Jet powerplants produce no audible exhaust noise until objectives or ground observers are very closely approached. No visible trails of exhaust flame are produced after dark, once complete combustion is attained. These two factors are highly desirable from the military aspect.

(8) No continuous electrical ignition is required, thus eliminating a serious source of disturbance in radio transmission.

(9) As a minimum number of moving parts is incorporated in jet powerplants, lubrication requirements are somewhat less severe.

(10) Generally, the total weight of a jet powerplant is approximately one-third that of a conventional reciprocating engine of equivalent performance characteristics.

(11) Actually, a higher value of operating efficiency is attained by jet powerplants while flying in the rarefied atmosphere of high altitudes. Power-off gliding angle is greatly improved due to absence of windmilling propeller drag.

(12) From a structural aspect, the jet-driven aircraft is exempted from the ground clearance limitations imposed by the standard lengths of conventional propeller blades. The consequent advantage is a lowered center of gravity for taxying and ground operations. This is

illustrated by Figure 4, in which (a) is a conventional, propeller-driven airplane, and (b) a jet-powered aircraft.

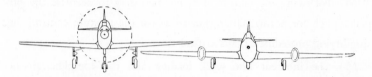

FIGURE 4. Elevation Views of Conventional Airplane and Jet-propelled Aircraft.

(13) Once the basic design of a jet-propelled aircraft is available, the structural and weight characteristics can be scaled either up or down with very little difficulty.

(14) A wide variety of safe fuels of low volatility are available for utilization with jet powerplants.

(15) The "power off" gliding range of jet-powered aircraft is greatly increased over that of conventional piston-engined aircraft, due to the complete absence of propeller drag.

DISADVANTAGES OF JET-PROPELLED POWERPLANTS

(1) The optimum operating efficiency of jet powerplants is not attained under forward velocities of the order of 400 miles per hour. At speeds below this minimum figure, the jet powerplant consumes practically twice as much fuel as does a conventional reciprocating engine of equivalent performance. Operating efficiency will attain the ideal value of 100 percent when the inlet and outlet velocities become identical, or, in other words, when the forward speed of the aircraft is equal to the velocity of its jet.

(2) Considerably lower values of brake thermal efficiency are reflected in the increased fuel consumption of jet powerplants. However, this disadvantage is offset, to some degree at least, by the fact that cheaper and more elemental fuels are employed for jet powerplant operation. More than a pound of fuel per 100 pounds of weight is consumed at take-off.

(3) The jetted hot combustion gases constitute a fire hazard in the immediate vicinity of the jet orifice. In general, areas closer than 20 feet to the rear of the jet powerplants are danger zones.

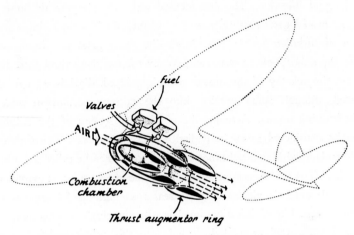

FIGURE 5.   The Action of the Thrust-augmentor Ring.

(4) Serious loss results from the exhaust combustion gases being normally ejected from the exit point of the jet orifice at a velocity considerably higher than that at which the aircraft is flying. As a consequence, a high degree of turbulence is created in the immediate vicinity of the jet orifice, with a resultant heavy reduction in thrust force. This condition, however, can be alleviated, to some extent, through the provision of a thrust augmentor ring, which comprises a venturi tube with thin, narrowed-down rear edges. It increases the velocity of the atmospheric air immediately surrounding the jet orifice up to the point where it equalizes the velocity of the jetted combustion gases. The turbulence can be greatly reduced in this manner, thus increasing the amount of power available for transformation to thrust. This device, which is also called the jet ejector, can effect thrust increases as high as 25 percent at low forward velocities, and 50 percent, at high forward velocities of the aircraft. However, a serious disadvantage of the jet ejector is its inability to provide an immediate

thrust increase under sudden acceleration. Accordingly, the current trend is toward more adaptable forms of thrust augmentation. The principal methods employed at the present time include afterburning and liquid injection. The first method utilizes the excess air present in the heated gases passing from the turbine unit into the tailpipe section of turbojet powerplants. Normally, these gases are discharged into the atmosphere as waste energy. By forcing them through a diffuser, the velocity of the heated gases is reduced. Fuel is then introduced, through spray nozzles, into the tailpipe section in which afterburning occurs. Actually, the afterburner section of the tailpipe can be considered as an individual ramjet powerplant. The turbojet powerplant, with an afterburner attached, could then be called a "turbo-ramjet." The fuel consumption attending the afterburning is extremely high, although it yields thrust increases as high as 50 percent in some cases. Liquid injection involves the spraying of water, usually mixed with ethyl or methyl alcohol, into the turbojet inlet duct in order to prevent high-altitude freezing. Due to the evaporation of this liquid, the temperature of the compressed air is lowered. This means a closer approach to ideal isothermal compression. In addition, the reduced temperature of the air entering the combustion chamber permits the burning of a greater amount of fuel, with an attendant increase in mass flow. Thrust increases approximating 30 percent have been obtained by liquid injection.

(5) The absence of a propeller slip-stream blast against the rear control surfaces makes ground taxying more difficult. Therefore, it is imperative to equip jet-driven aircraft with a tricycle-type landing-gear structure.

(6) Due to the high performance characteristics of jet-propelled aircraft, high acceleration forces of the order of 4 G's and over are quickly attained, with serious blackout complications as a direct result.

(7) A basic problem of the jet powerplant design is the conflicting requirement for a jet sufficiently large to permit an adequate

mechanical efficiency, and yet sufficiently small to allow high enough temperatures. The solution of this problem can be, at best, a compromise.

(8) Whereas the reciprocating engine makes available its maximum power for the takeoff, the maximum power output of the jet powerplant is attained only at maximum air speed. This condition imposes the necessity of lengthened takeoff runs for jet-propelled aircraft.

(9) Aircraft turbojet powerplants are subject to "blow out," which is reflected in the failure to support properly combustion at certain critical combinations of altitude and turbo speed. This unfavorable condition has been found, in some designs, at altitudes as low as 12,000 feet and at turbo speeds within a "dead band," ranging roughly from 5,000 to 11,500 revolutions per minute. The increased velocity of the air passing from the compressor to the combustion chambers is responsible for blow out. This high-velocity air restricts the temperature rise through the combustion chambers to the point where it becomes inadequate for further powerplant operation. This difficulty can be overcome by higher compressor pressures. These are available through multistage compressors, but at the expense of a high proportion of the total turbine output. A newly developed "supersonic compressor," which provides high pressures in a single stage, should prove useful in this connection. Alternate solutions for the prevention of blow out include: improved combustion-chamber design; variable-area fuel nozzles; fuel-flow redesign; and new fuels

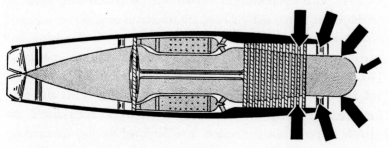

FIGURE 6. Inlet-duct Icing on an Axial-flow Turbojet Powerplant.

which allow better efficiency at high altitude. Also, improved ignition systems have made possible relights up to altitudes of approximately 35,000 feet.

(10) Icing on aircraft turbine powerplants is a more critical issue, particularly with axial-flow units, on which ice build-up drastically decreases the air flow. This disadvantage is, however, compensated for, to some extent, by the fact that the turbine-type powerplant can carry adequate deicing (as well as cabin pressurization, etc.) facilities and can still save 500 to 600 pounds of independent auxiliaries, when compared with a conventional piston engine of similar size and performance. The critical nature of jet icing becomes perceptible from the fact that the jet powerplant consumes 60 pounds of air for every pound of fuel burned. The reciprocating engine burns approximately 14 pounds of air for every pound of fuel burned. Thus, the jet powerplant consumes nearly five times the amount of air. When this air is moisture-laden, the resulting ice accumulation deprives the jet powerplant of air for both combustion and critical cooling purposes.

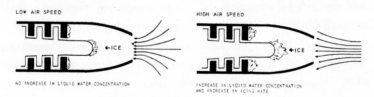

FIGURE 7. The Effect of Airspeed on Icing.

(11) Vital components of aircraft turbojet powerplants, including compressors, ducts, and diffusers, are subject to surging, i.e., a pulsating flow which occurs during operation of both centrifugal-flow and axial-flow compressors. Surging is responsible for two undesirable conditions. It induces destructive vibrations which may cause failure of highly stressed powerplant components. Surging causes also pressure-recovery losses in these components. As a direct result, the power output of the powerplant is reduced and the fuel consumption is increased. Beyond the peak point of the surge cycle, the flow-out

of the compressor stops and begins to reverse, that is, air flows back through the compressor because the pressure in the receiver is higher than in the compressor. Surging can be prevented by one of the following three methods: (1) by inserting additional piping between the compressor and the receiver; (2) by proper design of the diffuser inlets or by redesign of the compressor blades; or, (3) by reduction of the volume of the accumulating receiver. Method (1) has unfavorable features in that it reduces the pressure delivered to the receiver because of increased frictional losses through the additional piping. These remedies have all been tried in the various phases of turbojet research. Still another means of avoiding surging involves the provision of an auxiliary valve to bypass a portion of the delivered flow. While quite suitable for regulation, this arrangement would result in power waste because of the flow of compressed air through the bypass.

From this discussion, which presents an unbiased comparison of the jet-propelled aircraft powerplant with conventional sources of power, it might be deduced that, although there are many features in favor of the jet powerplant for aircraft use, it is difficult to abandon the reliable and economical reciprocating engine, but for the one serious drawback of the breakdown of propeller efficiency at high rotating speeds.

The Four Categories of Jet Powerplants

Reactive propulsion powerplants are classified into four basic categories, i.e., the aeroduct (ramjet and resojet), the turbojet, the propjet, and the rocketjet. Units of the first category consist essentially of an open tube in which a suitable fuel is burned, combined with the inrushing atmospheric air. The exit orifice, shaped as a venturi throat, gives the exhaust gases a rearward impetus. All jet powerplants having no compressor belong to this class. These units are designed for high performance and require extremely high forward velocities for a steady supply of atmospheric air for combustion. Some form of rocket assist or mechanical boost is required in order to start units of the aeroduct type.

The turbojet comprises a gas turbine which actuates an air compressor, which, in turn, furnishes the air required for the complete combustion of the fuel and for cooling the turbine-compressor combination. The combustion gases are directed against turbine rotor blades prior to being ejected through the rear exit orifice where they generate the reactive force which impels the aircraft forward. Since the turbojet powerplant relies on the turbocompressor unit, rather than on high-velocity ram atmospheric air, for the continuous supply of oxygen to support combustion, this type of jet powerplant is designed for performance closer approaching normal operating ranges.

The propjet consists of a conventional turbojet powerplant in which the central shaft, on which the turbocompressor units revolve, is extended forward to accommodate an aircraft propeller. This primary notion becomes subject to certain reservations as we progress in the book. Forward motion of the propjet-powered aircraft is derived from a combination of the thrust of the propeller and the thrust contributed by the rearward-directed, jetted combustion gases. Some turboprop powerplants function merely as gas turbines, all their output being utilized to rotate an aircraft propeller. No jet thrust is exerted by these types and, therefore, they are not classified as jet-propelled powerplants.

The rocket jet differs from the thermal jet powerplants previously described in that it contains all the elements required for complete combustion of its fuel. Transporting its own oxygen supply, in addition to either a liquid fuel or a relatively slow-burning powder, it is a completely self-sustaining unit. As the thermal jet powerplants, the rocketjet derives its thrust from the reactive force generated by the rearward-directed jet of high-pressure, high-temperature gases which propel the craft forward.

It is likely that in the future, the propjet, which is a combination of a turbojet and a conventional aircraft propeller, will serve as the aircraft for performances under 500 miles per hour and altitudes under 30,000 feet. For performance ranges of 500 to 800 miles per hour, in all probability, the basic turbojet will be employed. For a performance beyond these ranges, the aeroresonator and the rocketjet will undoubtedly furnish the essential velocity and climb characteristics.

Chapter 2

COMPRESSORLESS JET POWERPLANTS

The Aeroresonator

One basic form of the thermal jet powerplant is the aeroresonator, more commonly called the resojet or pulsejet. This air-stream engine can be considered an intermittent-firing duct, which, in general, has only one moving part, a flap valve located at its forward extremity. This valve consists of a multiple grid, or grille, resembling a series of unbalanced shutters. The flap opens intermittently for the admission of atmospheric air and is closed by the detonation created by the combustion of the air and fuel mixture within the engine duct. In powerplants of this type, the fuel-sprayer nozzles are located directly in the rear of the air-valve assembly, while the actuating spark plug lies still farther to the rear in a lengthened venturi section.

The operating cycle of the aeroresonator involves periodic explosions of the fuel-air mixture, which produce the requisite high pressures in the open conduit. For optimum efficiency, these explosions must be maintained in resonance with the compression-wave period of the conduit system. In operation, the indrawn atmospheric air is mixed with a suitable fuel, compressed in the following stage by the compression wave produced by the previous explosion, and, finally, ignition

20

and combustion of the fuel-air mixture is effected at high temperature and pressure.

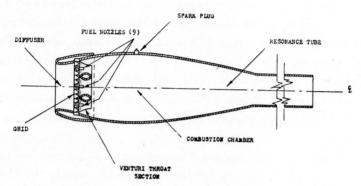

FIGURE 8. Cross Section of an Aeroresonator Powerplant.

THE THREE PHASES OF THE PULSEJET CYCLE

The operating cycle of the pulsejet powerplant has three phases: the charging phase, the exploding phase, and the replenishing phase, which will be analyzed in the order in which they occur. For the charging phase, the aircraft must be in motion of sufficiently high forward velocity to cause the atmospheric air to be rammed into the propulsion duct. The inrushing atmospheric air builds up a positive pressure in the diffuser section, which opens the automatic flap valves, as indicated in figure 9. From the diffuser, the slightly compressed air flows into the gas-combustion chamber, into which the fuel is simultaneously injected.

The heated walls of the combustion chamber ignite the fuel-air mixture to initiate the exploding phase. The single spark plug ignites the charge when the powerplant is started. The explosion attending the combustion causes a considerable increase in pressure which seals the air inlets by actuating the automatic flap valves. The products of combustion are violently ejected from the jet orifice at the rear of the tailpipe, where they generate the reactive thrust force.

The replenishing phase depends on the inertia of the ejected combustion gases to effect a reduction of the air pressure within the combustion chamber to a value somewhat below atmospheric. Then, the automatic grid flap valves are reopened by the higher pressure of the external stream of atmospheric air. In this manner, a fresh charge of atmospheric air is rammed in through the jet intake orifice. From this point, the cycle of operations is repeated. The frequency of these processes is about 40 to 50 per second in the present design of the resojet powerplant. Figure 9 illustrates the phases of the resojet cycle: (a) is the charging phase: if the aeroresonator powerplant is in motion, the force of the inrushing air builds up pressure in the diffuser. The flapper valves are open, and atmospheric air is admitted into the venturi section to mix with fuel from the nine fuel nozzles; (b) illustrates the exploding phase: the hot walls of the combustion chamber ignite the fuel-air mixture which explodes, thus sealing all the inlets. The resultant gas pressure creates the reactive thrust which imparts forward motion to the powerplant; (c) is the replenishing phase: the inertia of the escaping gases reduces the pressure in the combustion chamber to a value below atmospheric. This partial vacuum causes the grid flapper valves to reopen.

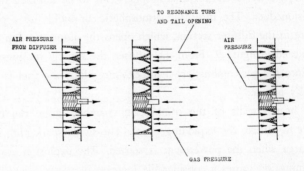

FIGURE 9.　The three Successive Phases of the Pulsejet Operating Cycle.

The pulsating noise of the exhaust, characteristic of resojet powerplants, is necessarily intermittent because of the intermittent nature of the combustion following the initial ignition of the fuel-air mixture by the single spark plug. This characteristic of the resojet is responsible for its sobriquet of "stuttering stovepipe." The exhaust pulsations of the reciprocating engine are very similar to those of the resojet powerplant.

The intermittent combustion in the resojet cycle and the lack of a positive method of compressing adequate air to support combustion indicate a low value of thermodynamic efficiency. This is one of the disadvantages of all types of jet-propelled aircraft powerplants, in general. However, the extremely low weight and simplicity of design of the resojet offset, to a great extent, the lowered operating efficiency. The simplicity of design is reflected in economy of material and production time, which are of great importance in national emergency.

One limiting factor of pulsejet velocity is the blunt forward extremity of this aircraft. The attendant drag is necessarily high. Recent research has indicated that a shroud, placed so as to envelop the entire pulsejet powerplant, minimizes this difficulty. Intake air is thus allowed to expand and decelerate. The air surrounding the inlet valve in the shrouded pulsejet is prevented from attaining the critical velocity values at which drag may overcome thrust. This condition is maintained even at high forward speeds.

The pulsejet is a dependable powerplant. Its important production and maintenance advantages are that its control is achieved solely through fuel metering. No complex governor devices, injectors, and carburetors are required. The grid flap valve is comparatively short lived because of the frequency and severity of its operation. Some engines require replacement of this vital component after ¾-hour operation. Fuel consumption of the pulsejet, although lower than that of the ramjet, is still well above that of the turbojet powerplant.

Figure 10 illustrates the "V-1" *Ver Geltungswaffe* pilotless aircraft with an aeroresonator powerplant. The parts shown are as follows: 1 warhead (capacity approximately 1,000 kilograms); 2 fuel-filler cap; 3 lifting lug; 4 fuel tank (capacity 130 gallons); 5 wire-bound, spherical compressed-air bottles, delivering fuel under pressure;

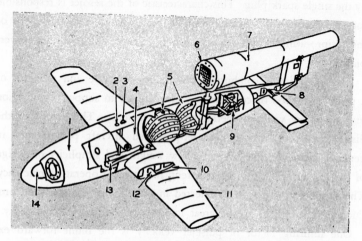

FIGURE 10. The German "V-1" Pilotless Aircraft.

6 grill incorporating shutters, or flapper valves, and fuel-injection nozzles; 7 impulse-duct (aeroresonator) powerplant; 8 pneumatic servo-mechanism operating rudder and elevators; 9 automatic pilot, three air-driven gyros, altitude and range-setting controls; 10 pressed-metal wing ribs; 11 metal tubular main spar; 12 launching rail; 14 light metal alloy nose fairing.

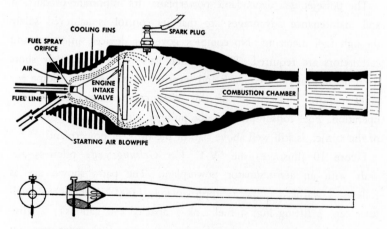

FIGURE 11. Sections through Compressorless Jet Powerplants.

THE ATHOYD

The "Athoyd," which name is an abbreviation of "aero thermodynamic duct," differs from members of the aeroresonator family in that its firing cycle is not intermittent, but continuous. The athoyd, or "ramjet," is the simplest form of jet powerplant. It consists essentially of an open tube, or pipe, in the form of a venturi nozzle. It contains a fuel injector and a single spark plug. The ram jet, like all aeroduct jets, operates only at high forward speeds, when atmospheric air is caused to flow through the main duct at high velocity. A restriction in the inlet orifice of the ramjet momentarily slows down the incoming atmospheric air, which is simultaneously compressed by the air particles which are still moving from behind at a high velocity. This provides a ramming action. Liquid fuel is injected into the mass of compressed air, and the fuel-air mixture is ignited and burned. Heat is added at constant pressure, in a manner different from that of the pulsejet cycle where heating is effected at constant volume. Expansion of the heated combustion gases occurs in the after portion of the ramjet unit which is flared as a venturi tube. As a consequence, the velocity of these combustion gases is greatly increased and they are forcibly ejected through the rear orifice. It is characteristic of the ramjet, as of all aeroducts, that the air is ejected at a considerably higher velocity than the speed of the entering air stream. This provides the reaction which yields the forward motion.

The ramjet powerplant, being the simplest form of heat engine as yet devised, has no moving parts and, therefore, needs no lubrication. In one successful ramjet design which develops a thrust force equal to 2,200 horsepower, the total weight of the complete unit is 70 pounds. This corresponds to about ½ ounce per horsepower for this craft, which can fly at speeds of 800 to 1,500 miles per hour. Optimum operating efficiencies of all varieties of ramjet powerplants occur between 1,000 and 1,500 miles per hour. Some form of rocket-assist device or catapult is necessary to initially boost the ramjet up to these efficient operating speeds.

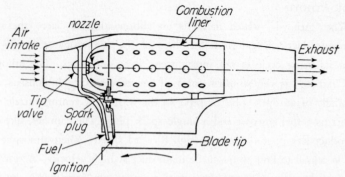

FIGURE 12. General Electric "3R-1" Helicopter Ramjet Powerplant.

A very recent variety of the ramjet powerplant is called the "intermittent ramjet." This acts rather like the pulsejet, except that it is not equipped with a drag-producing shutter valve. Fuel is injected in quick slugs, rather than continuously. Each fuel charge is mixed with incoming air. Then it moves progressively along the barrel of the powerplant, until it is exploded by the igniter plug. The resultant explosion not only provides reactive thrust, but also compresses the following fuel-air charge.

We have already observed that one of the salient disadvantages of the ramjet is the requirement of an initial velocity, i.e., some form of launching device. Successful experiments have been conducted with the "rocketram," which consists essentially of a self-sustaining rocket mechanism located just behind the standard ramjet inlet orifice. The rocket provides the ramjet with fuel in the form of unburned gases for starting. In addition, air for the combustion of the ramjet's own fuel supply is drawn into the inlet orifice because of the reduced pressure in the ramjet barrel. This arrangement precludes the necessity for high initial speed. The rocket ramjet can start itself.

As it has been mentioned previously, the aeroduct aircraft powerplants have the advantage of simple design and low weight for the thrust and power developed. These units are not adaptable to low-speed aircraft. Their optimum operation occurs at such a high velocity that some form of rocket-assist or catapult device is required for their starting.

PHYSICAL LIMITATIONS OF COMPRESSORLESS JETS

The low thermodynamic efficiency of aeroduct powerplants is their greatest disadvantage. Since the aeroduct units do not have a compressor, the greater proportion of the heat furnished to the air should be supplied at an elevated air temperature to insure a satisfactory thermodynamic efficiency. The jet-powerplant designer is forced to make a compromise. If the jet is heavy, the available heat will not bring it up to the required elevated temperatures and the efficiency will be lowered. Conversely, if the jet is very light, even though its temperature is adequately high, its thermodynamic efficiency will be only apparent, as the lighter the jet, the smaller is its mechanical efficiency. From this, it is obvious that, even where the heat available for a certain specified value of thrust can be predetermined, the jet weight per pound per second of the thrust is severely limited. Therefore, the aeroduct powerplant cannot be adapted to low-performance, low-powered aircraft, since this application would require a jet of comparatively large proportions.

However, although the aeroduct powerplant cannot develop effective power at low values of forward velocity, it is, nevertheless, the best powerplant for overcoming the high fuel consumption rates of supersonic flight. Some modification of the aeroduct unit could be incorporated in an aircraft, the performance of which could be made to approach the speed of sound by other, more conventional powerplants. Having attained this point, the jet units could then be actuated to help pass the sonic barrier.

In operation, the aeroduct powerplant is started by an electrical ignition, or glow plug, similar in design to the conventional spark plug. The electrical energy for starting is furnished by a ground-installed battery. Once started, the exit orifice of the aeroduct emits a rich yellow exhaust flame throughout the initial period until the source of external-air supply is cut off. From this point onward, the powerplant operates with a blue flame and the exhaust roar becomes much louder as the gradually increased thrust force is developed. The flame trail extends 30 to 40 feet at initial firing. Then it is reduced to 15 or 20 feet as firing progresses. When the proper relationship between air speed and fuel speed is obtained, the flame trail disappears entirely.

The noise accompanying aeroduct powerplant operation is a serious tactical disadvantage for military application. The fuel consumption rate is very high, second only to that of the rocketjet powerplant. However, a conventional reciprocating engine, were it capable of operating at high supersonic speeds, would have a comparable fuel consumption per mile. The ability of the aeroduct powerplant to produce increasing power at increasing speed adapts it admirably to high-speed supersonic flight.

Chapter 3

THE TURBOJET POWERPLANT

OPERATION OF THE ELEMENTAL TURBOJET

It has been demonstrated that the aeroduct powerplant cannot attain its optimum operating efficiency only at elevated values of forward velocity. This condition, which automatically precludes the employment of the aeroduct in low-performance, low-powered aircraft, has been attributed primarily to the fact that units of this category accomplish the intake and compression of the atmospheric air required for combustion by their extremely rapid forward motion. If it were possible to provide some internal means of furnishing combustion air under compression in the main duct of the jet powerplant, a far more extensive range of usable operating efficiencies of jet powerplants would be available.

This objective is accomplished in the turbojet powerplant. The combustion process in a basic turbojet powerplant is illustrated in figure 13. Atmospheric air for combustion enters on both sides and close to the axis of the rotor of the compressor unit. The rotor vanes hurl the air outward toward the circumference. The air is forced out of the impeller at a velocity of about 1,500 feet per second and a temperature of about 400° F. The flow of the air stream is thus accelerated to velocities approaching supersonic value.

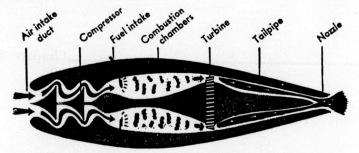

FIGURE 13. Principle of the Thermal Turbojet Powerplant.

A helical volute or spiral-shaped diffuser collects the air and converts the velocity head of the air mass into pressure head. The air is then conducted into a spiral combustion chamber of increasing cross section where approximately 22 percent of the air is mixed with the injected fuel (by far the greater proportion of the air mass being utilized to cool the internal components of the powerplant). Combustion is then effected in the ignition pipe. The combustion gases are ejected from the ignition pipe and forced through a venturi nozzle, undergoing a high degree of expansion. While in this expanded state, the heated combustion gases are directed against the turbine rotor blades and thus actuate an internal-combustion turbine unit. Roughly, five eighths, or 62.6 percent, of the total heat energy evolved is utilized for the operation of the turbine unit. The turbine, in turn, drives the compressor.

The combustion gases which, up to this point, have utilized only a portion of their potential energy, are still at an elevated temperature and above atmospheric pressure. Leaving the tips of the turbine rotor blades, they are led through the exit channel to the rear jet orifice. This orifice, or final exit point, is designed, as in the case of the jet powerplants previously described, as a venturi nozzle so shaped as to greatly increase the velocity of the exhaust gases. Each second, approximately 71 pounds of heated air and gases leave the rear jet orifice with an exit velocity of about 1,800 feet per second. As in the earlier models, the recoil which imparts forward motion to the aircraft is generated by these rapidly jetted gases.

It is obvious that the turbojet powerplant functions in exactly the same manner as the simple aeroduct unit described in the preceding pages, but, in addition, it can also compress its combustion air and thus start from a standstill.

FIGURE 14. Axial-flow Turbojet Powerplant
(The General Electric-Allison "TG-180").

AXIAL- AND CENTRIFUGAL-FLOW CHARACTERISTICS

The elemental turbojet unit of figure 13 does not illustrate the high-power-output units now in use. It has been inserted only to simplify the understanding of the operating cycle of the turbojet powerplant. In actual practice, there are two main categories of turbojet powerplants; the centrifugal-flow type and the axial-flow type. Each type has certain advantages and certain disadvantages. A comparison of the two types shows that the centrifugal-flow turbojet has a large frontal area, a large-diameter compressor, and multiple combustion chambers, which are responsible for the disadvantage of increased drag. However, this type has the advantage of low weight. The axial-flow turbojet power plant, being equipped with a small-diameter compressor, has the dual advantage of straight-line flow and a slender contour. The first factor is reflected in more effective ramming, the second in greatly lowered drag. However, the total weight of the axial-flow turbojet is much larger. Auxiliary and accessory units of an axial-flow assembly are more sensitive to bleeding than are the centrifugal types. We have already observed that the axial-flow turbojet is also more susceptible to icing. In general, however, at the present stage of development, little definite superiority for either type can be established.

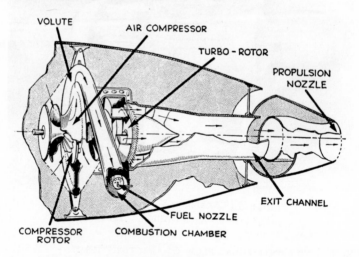

FIGURE 15. Cut-away Drawing of a Centrifugal-flow Turbojet Powerplant.

A centrifugal-flow turbojet powerplant, in which the combustion air has a centrifugal-flow pattern, is illustrated in figure 15. The compressor impeller is double sided, air entering the compressor through circumferential inlets at both the front and back of the impeller member. Single-sided impellers are also employed in some designs.

At the present stage of development, it appears preferable to equip large turbojet units, designed for high power output, with compressors which impart axial flow to the relatively large volume of air required. For higher operating efficiencies, a multistage compressor unit must be employed. As many as nine to sixteen stages of compression are used. The internal combustion turbine, employed as the prime mover in the aircraft turbojet powerplant, operates either on the single-stage or multi-stage principle.

FIGURE 16. The First Turbojet Powerplant (the British Whittle "W.2").

IMPELLER BLADE DESIGN

The contour of the impeller blades of the axial-flow compressor resembles that of a miniature airfoil section. This cross section is most effective because of the small pressure drop and the large gas volume involved. The axial-flow compressor looks like a straight re-action turbine with alternate sets of stationary and rotating blades. However, the action of the compressor blades in the axial-flow com-pressor is a direct reverse of the expansion process in the reaction turbine. An important feature of the axial-flow compressor is that, though it is small, it can supply a large output volume, with an accompanying high degree of efficiency. The fluid to be compressed is made to flow axially through the casing of the compressor.

The compressor installed in aircraft turbojet powerplants is assumed

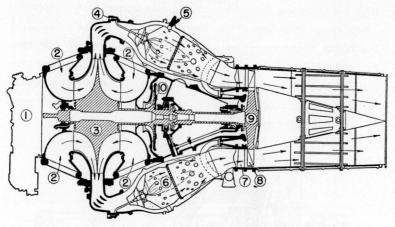

FIGURE 17. The Pratt and Whitney "J-42"
Centrifugal-flow Turbojet Powerplant.

to absorb up to approximately 75 percent of the power developed by the turbine rotor. Research and development seek to reduce this figure, thus to improve considerably turbine-compressor relationship. One solution would be the utilization of the ramming effect of introducing atmospheric air forcibly into the air-intake vent when jet-propelled aircraft is flying at high rates of forward velocity. This would greatly lower the peak loads imposed on the compressor unit.

Compression ratios in turbojet powerplants generally vary between 3.18:1 and 5.0:1. The use of the newly developed "Two spool," or split, compressor heralds compression ratios as high as 12.0:1.

GAS TURBINES

Since the turbine is an important basic element of the powerplant, a brief review of internal-combustion turbine design and operating principles will be given at this point.

The internal-combustion or gas turbine is a simple form of heat engine, consisting essentially of a rotor, mounted on a central shaft. The outer circumference of the rotor is fitted with turbine blades, the cross section of each corresponding to a miniature airfoil section. These

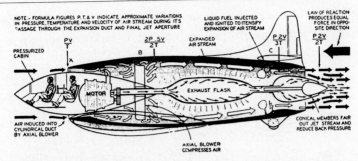

FIGURE 18. Pressure, Temperature and Velocity Relationships of Air throughout the Turbojet Operating Cycle.

turbine blades are set at such an angle that they can be rotated by the heated combustion gases, directed against them through a suitable nozzle or duct. The highly-stressed root element of the blade is usually shaped as a "ball" or as a "fir tree." Aviation gas turbines are most commonly equipped with reaction-type turbine blading, which consists of alternate sets of stationary and rotating blades. In the reaction turbine, the expansion of the heated combustion gases occurs either partially or completely within the moving series of blades, as distinguished from the impulse type of turbine in which expansion occurs within stationary nozzles or guide-vane passages.

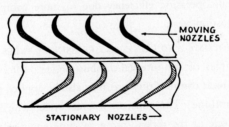

FIGURE 19. Layout of a Reaction-turbine Blading.

A successful application of the internal-combustion turbine is the turbo-supercharger unit. The flow of hot combustion gases for operating the turbo-supercharger is furnished by the exhaust of the reciprocating engine on which the unit is installed. The gas turbine actuating the compressor of the aircraft turbojet powerplant differs from the turbo-supercharger unit in that it functions entirely as a prime mover.

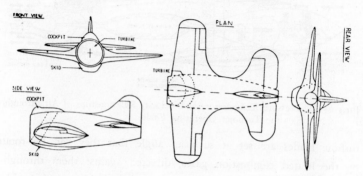

FIGURE 20. The German "Heinkel T" Jet-propelled Aircraft.

The primary advantages of the internal-combustion turbine, as compared to the reciprocating internal-combustion engine, are as follows: (1) higher rotative velocity at the power take-off shaft; (2) simplified lubrication system, as there are fewer moving parts; (3) higher power output per unit; (4) more constant torque due to the complete absence of inertia forces, as there are no moving members that rapidly reverse their direction of motion; and (5) a potential gain in overall operating efficiency due to more complete expansion of the combustion gases.

CONSTANT-VOLUME AND CONSTANT-PRESSURE CYCLES

The principles of the internal-combustion, i.e., combustion at constant volume or at constant pressure, may also be applied to the internal-combustion turbine. The constant-volume cycle, which is similar to the normal cycle of the reciprocating gasoline engine, is the actuating cycle of the Holzwarth, or explosion type, gas turbine. With this cycle, the operation of the turbine is intermittent, since combustion occurs within a closed chamber. Valves, or some other forms of periodic distributing devices, are consequently required to bring the combustion gases into direct contact with the turbine rotor blades.

The constant-pressure cycle is the actuating cycle of the Diesel, or compression-ignition, engine with certain modifications. In gas-turbine

FIGURE 21. *Internal Section of the J-48 Turbojet:* Air is drawn in through the inlet screen (A) and guide vanes (B) and then compressed by the impeller (C).

operation, the constant-pressure cycle requires some external means for compressing the combustion air, since combustion occurs in open passages between the compressor and the turbine. In the constant-pressure cycle, the operation involves a steady flow of fuel-air mixture to the combustion chamber and a steady discharge of combustion gases through the turbine nozzles or ducts.

From this it is clear that the constant-volume, or explosion, turbine requires lower compression pressure for satisfactory operation and is

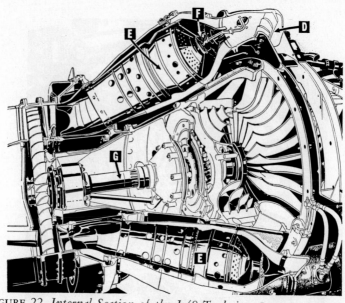

FIGURE 22. *Internal Section of the J-48 Turbojet:* Compressed air is introduced through the inlet duct (D) to the conical burners (E), mixes with fuel injected by fuel nozzle (F), and is burned; the turbine shaft (G) connects the turbine and impeller components.

easier to cool. Reduction in casing temperatures lends itself well to air cooling in the constant-volume turbine, since, when there is a substantial pressure reduction in the combustion chamber, cooling air can be forced against the turbine rotor blades through the turbine nozzles before the cycle of operations is again resumed.

Temperatures are prevented from becoming excessive in the constant-pressure gas turbine by supplying an excess of air for cooling. Therefore, in aircraft internal-combustion turbines, as much as 600 percent excess air is supplied for both combustion and cooling. This air-cooling process imposes a considerable amount of negative work, since a large proportion of the total power developed by the turbine is used for the operation of a large-capacity air compressor. Air cooling also reduces the temperature of the combustion gases considerably, which results in correspondingly lower values of brake thermal efficiency.

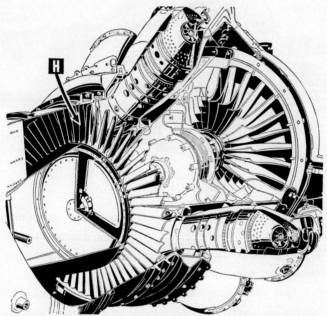

FIGURE 23. *Internal Section of the J-48 Turbojet:* Expanding gases flow through turbine blades (h), thus rotating the shaft, and then through the tailpipe to provide propulsive thrust.

However, because of the intermittent action of the constant-volume gas turbine, it cannot yield a constant torque as does the constant-pressure unit. Another drawback of the constant-volume turbine is its tendency to very rapid reduction in gas velocity during the expansion period, which lowers the average turbine efficiency. For these reasons, the constant-pressure internal-combustion turbine is utilized almost exclusively in modern turbojet powerplant designs.

The primary difficulty of the application of a gas turbine as a prime mover for aircraft propulsion has been the lack of resistance of construction materials to the severe conditions of high temperature encountered in turbine operations. The casing temperature to which the

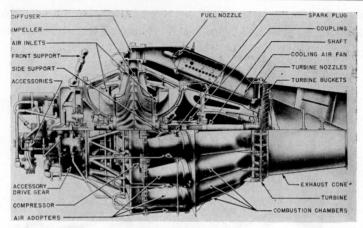

FIGURE 24. Centrifugal-flow Turbojet Powerplant
(The General Electric-Allison "I-40").

internal structural members are subjected consists of the initial temperature of the combustion gases as they are discharged from the turbine nozzles and of friction, eddy, and windage losses which are also transformed into heat. Since casing temperatures much higher than 1,200° F. have been encountered, and the tensile strength of the majority of available steels has been reduced by 50 percent at 1,000° F., the problem has been a metallurgical, rather than a mechanical one. The discovery of new, stronger, and otherwise improved construction materials made possible the application of the turbojet powerplant for aircraft.

INDICATOR DIAGRAMS

The constant-pressure cycle is illustrated in figure 25, in which I to II represents the combustion period which occurs at constant pressure; II to III represents power, or expansion; III to IV is the exhaust phase in which the waste products of combustion are eliminated at constant pressure; and IV to I represents the compression of the fresh intake charge which proceeds simultaneously with the exhaust phase.

Figure 27 is a more detailed illustration of the pressure-volume or

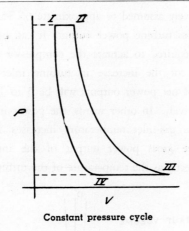

Constant pressure cycle

FIGURE 25. Indicator Diagram of the internal-combustion
Constant-pressure Cycle.

indicator diagram for the constant-pressure gas-turbine cycle. It has
been previously stated that the gross power output of the internal-
combustion turbine will vary directly as the temperature of the combustion gases at the turbine inlet. This can be verified graphically.
The indicator diagram shows that, at a gas-inlet temperature of 1,000°
F., the combustion gases will expand after ignition of the fuel-air
mixture from an initial limit of approximately 9 cubic feet to a final
limit of approximately 24 cubic feet, the total expansion being 15
cubic feet. Now, if we assume that the temperature of the turbine
inlet gases is raised to 1,500° F., then the combustion gases will
expand from approximately 12 cubic feet to 32.5 cubic feet, or, the
total expansion will be 20.5 cubic feet. The initial and final pressure
limits are identical in both cases, namely, 45 pounds per square inch
and zero, respectively. It then follows that the average pressures will
be also equal in both cases. The energy released during the expansion
periods of the two cases treated increases in direct proportion to
the increase in volume. The gross turbine power outputs can be assumed to be proportional to the increases in volume, i.e., the ratio is
15 to 20.5. The negative work, or power absorbed by the compressor,

can be conservatively assumed to approximate 66 ⅔ percent, or two-thirds, of the gross turbine power output. It can be also established that the power required to actuate the compressor will remain constant irrespective of the increase in turbine inlet-gas temperature. Then, the ratio of net power outputs will be 5 to 10.5 at 1,000 and 1,500° F., respectively. In other words, the power increases over 100 percent when the gas-inlet temperature increases 50 percent. This indicates that the gross power output of the internal-combustion turbine varies directly as the temperature of the turbine inlet gases.

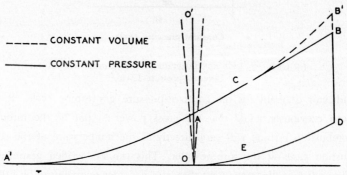

FIGURE 26. *Temperature-entropy Diagram:* O-O' represents the axis of zero entropy, progressive changes in the characteristics of the working substance being designated by the displacements indicated. O-A indicates compression of the fresh charge adiabatically. O-A' indicates compression of the fresh charge isothermally. C indicates the initial point of combustion, the process following along the lines of constant volume or constant pressure as the case may be. B or B'-D indicates adiabatic expansion. E indicates the condition of the exhaust gases after being utilized for regenerative processes in cases where regeneration is employed.

The diagram of figure 18 indicates the approximate pressure, temperature, and velocity relationships of the air during the operating cycle of the turbojet powerplant. The aircraft shown is the Italian "Caproni-Campini C-2," in which the compressor unit is actuated by a conventional, reciprocating, radial aircraft engine.

A similar thermodynamic reasoning can be applied to the atmospheric air introduced into the compressor, since its temperature also exerts a pronounced influence on gas-turbine cycle efficiency. At the same time, the capacity will vary approximately 4 percent for the same 10° F. variation in the air-inlet temperature.

Specific fuel consumption, which is a function of the air-inlet temperature, is about 1.12 pounds per pound thrust per hour in routine turbojet operation. Consumption of 0.89 pounds per pound thrust per hour has also been obtained and it is expected that the fuel consumption will be further lowered to 0.80 pounds or less.

An increase in turbine air inlet temperature causes difficulties. Chief among these is the problem of adequately cooling internal structural components. Ceramics have proved invaluable in this respect. Some of these have over 10,000 and 15,000 pounds per square inch tensile strengths at temperatures of 1,800 and 1,900° F., respectively. However, internal temperatures of 3,000 to 3,500° F. approach the ideal more closely.

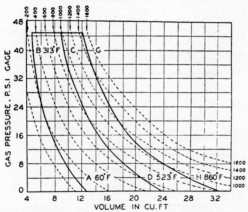

FIGURE 27. Indicator Diagram of a Constant-pressure internal-combustion Turbine.

The turbine blades cannot normally resist these elevated temperatures. Both air and liquid cooling of hollow blade elements has been attempted. Another measure is the provision of porous blade elements that can be sweat-cooled. For this purpose, powdered ferrous metals, alloyed with copper, have been molded at 150-ton pressure and then sintered at 2,000° F. The resultant product had an ultimate strength of about 100,000 pounds per square inch. Porous oxide ceramics may be also suitable for blades.

Although the liquid-cooled metal blade is undoubtedly superior from the aspect of temperature drop, its complex design, involving the supply of cooling water, suitable radiator, and extensive piping, may make the much simpler, finned, air-cooled blade system preferable.

COMBUSTION-CHAMBER DESIGN

The combustor or burner unit, several of which are spaced around

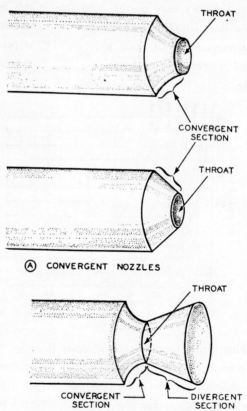

FIGURE 28. Representative Nozzle Sections.

the outer circumference of the turbojet powerplant, in the case of the centrifugal-flow type, or which may consist of a single ring, in the case of the axial-flow type, is the component in which the chemical energy of the fuel is converted into usable heat energy through its combustion in direct contact with excess air to obtain the operating temperatures desired. The heated gases, which are the direct products of the combustion, expand to a lower, near-atmospheric pressure within the turbine unit. A portion of the thermal energy of the gases is then transformed into mechanical energy at the turbine-rotor shaft. The cross section of the combustor may be comparatively small because its rate of heat release may be assumed to be quite high.

The combustion-chamber design is either the straight-through type or the reverse-flow type, depending on the flow of the air through the chamber. In the straight-through type, the air enters from the compressor end and flows through in the same direction to exit at the turbine end. In the second type, the air flow entering the combustion chamber is reversed.

There is a 3 to 5 pound pressure drop between the interior of the combustion chamber and the outside atmosphere. This explains why air tends to flow freely into the combustion chamber. Desirable features, which can be attained only by precise combustion-chamber design, include a low pressure drop and a high combustion efficiency.

THERMODYNAMIC CONSIDERATIONS

The simple turbine operating cycle must provide for the extremely high absolute temperatures encountered and which are essential for

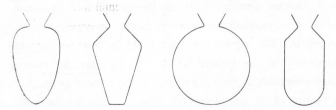

FIGURE 29. Combustion-chamber Outlines.

a high operating efficiency and power output. The heat of the initially expanding products of combustion is of the order of 1,700° F. At this temperature, the combustion gases will contain about 600 percent excess air. From this, the need for several stages of air compression is obvious. The rim of the turbine-rotor assembly is subjected to temperatures in the region of 1,200° F. Turbine operating efficiency increases in direct proportion to the rotation velocity of the turbine rotor up to a certain point, beyond which there is a rapid and pronounced reduction in efficiency. At the present stage of development, the optimum peripheral velocity for turbojet rotor blades appears to be that of sound, or, approximately 764 miles per hour. In the case of a turbine rotor blade of 24-inch diameter, the equivalent rotation speed would be approximately 12,000 revolutions per minute.

REGENERATION

In the future, we may anticipate the advent of aircraft turbojet powerplants developing considerably more thrust than is obtainable with currently manufactured units. Should these units yield sufficiently large power outputs to warrant the complications and added weight involved, they may be made to incorporate various forms of regenerative devices in order to minimize the inherent reduction in thermodynamic efficiency which has previously been discussed at some length. Regeneration processes tend to recover a considerable fraction of the heat energy dissipated in the turbine exhaust gases. This would increase overall turbine performance in that the thermal-energy waste could be used for heating the fresh charge after compression and also at constant pressure. This can be accomplished by means of a mechanical regenerator, or heat exchanger, generally operating in counterflow. The regenerator unit could be inserted between the compressor and the turbine where it could heat the entering air, after compression, to the temperature of the exhaust gases. Regenerative heating of the compressed air, however, increases the combustion and casing temperatures, or, if the casing temperature remains constant, it increases the amount of excess air essential for the prevention of too high temperatures. Recent experience with gas-turbine units has proved that approximately 15 percent of the total heat required is the maximum amount that can be recovered from the exhaust gases. With the passage of the air through the regenerator unit, the pressure will be considerably reduced. This pressure drop must be compensated

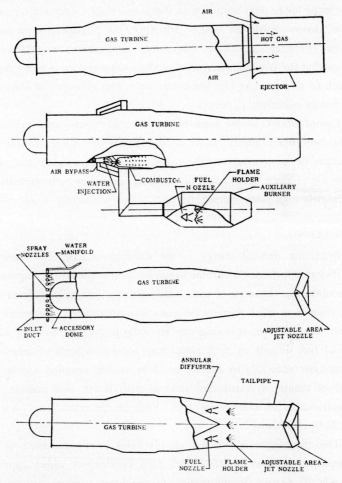

FIGURE 30. *Methods of Thrust Augmentation:* (a) jet ejector; (b) auxiliary burner; (c) liquid injection; (d) tailpipe afterburner.

for by the compressor, which thus must compress to a higher pressure, and, as a consequence, it will consume more power.

INTERCOOLERS

As an alternate solution, the heat exchanger could be replaced by an intercooler, in which case, the air would reenter the compressor at the same lower temperature as in the initial stage. Since the temperature increase results in reduced efficiency, the provision of an intercooler between successive stages of compression would reduce somewhat the power requirements of the compressor drive. As a direct result of this arrangement, the overall operating efficiency of the cycle would be materially increased.

Complications, in the form of much larger frontal area and drag, will most likely attend efforts to incorporate any form of heat exchanger or intercooler into the aircraft turbojet powerplant assembly. The use of these devices will be probably limited to turbojet units of extremely high power output.

REHEATING

Imparting thermal energy to the combustion gases by reheating as they pass through the turbine would be another method of improving the operating efficiency of the aircraft turbojet powerplant. Since the air content of these combustion gases is approximately 85 percent of their total volume, reheating can be accomplished by burning additional fuel directly in their path. Any acceptable form of reheating combustor adaptable to aircraft could be readily installed within the turbine casing or constructed integral with it. In this manner, the disadvantages of added weight and drag of the regenerative devices could be eliminated.

The afterburner, which has already been briefly discussed, is essentially a reheater. Initial afterburner installations added approximately 20 percent to the weight of the basic turbojet powerplant. Recent large-output turbojets have afterburners attached which practically double the length of the powerplant. "Flash power," comprising momentary bursts for emergency conditions or for combat maneuvers, is reflected in thrust increases as high as 50 percent. The rate of climb can be increased 50 percent for a given design. The afterburner also makes possible a 50 percent reduction in required takeoff distance. Afterburning imposes a penalty of 2 to 3 percent on cruise fuel consumption. The maximum benefit achieved for the cruise condition is estimated to be of the order of 10 to 12 percent. A higher value would indicate that turbine and compressor characteristics were inadequately matched. In actual operation, the turboramjet combination is a very flexible unit, because the afterburner can be cut out at will by the pilot, the basic engine then reverting to normal turbojet operation.

Turbojet powerplants aspirate five times the volume of air actually required for combustion. The additional volume of air is used for cooling. When an afterburner is installed, still more air is required, necessitating, in turn, larger intake orifices and ducting.

Gyroscopic Loads

The elevated rotational speeds and long, narrow configuration of aircraft turbojet engine shafts make these members particularly susceptible to severe gyroscopic loads. These loads are well under control during normal, level flight. However, a backward movement on the control column of the jet airplane causes the turbine shaft to resist the resulting climbing motion. This condition, in turn, impresses a down load on the front bearing, and, simultaneously, an up load on the rear bearing. Concurrently, as the nose section of the airplane climbs upward, the turbojet-engine shaft creates a force tending to yaw the aircraft to the right.

Diving the aircraft by pushing the control column forward would create a reverse gyroscopic force. The direct result of this force would be a yaw to the left. The last-mentioned actions introduced side loadings on the bearings and turbojet-engine shaft. The net effect could be complete bearing failure. Then, because of the restraint of the remaining bearing, there would be grave risk of failure also for the shaft.

The intensity of all these forces would increase drastically with maneuvers of high kinetic energy, such as violent pull-ups. The worst conditions, which must, of course, be provided against in the design of turbojet-engine shafts, are high-speed spins at full engine thrust. Such an operational condition may occur during the performance of violent acrobatics.

JET-ENGINE FUELS

The basic requirements for a suitable jet-aircraft fuel are as follows:

    (a) low cost per gallon

    (b) high BTU content per gallon

    (c) low flammability for safety

    (d) low volatility for fuel economy

    (e) availability

    (f) performance dependability

Aircraft turbojet powerplants apparently perform equally well with either gasoline (Specification ANF 28) or kerosene (Specification ANF 34) as fuel. According to the newer Specification ANF, jet-engine fuel requirements are as follows:

Freezing Point	Not above—76° F.
Aromatic Content	Not over 30 percent by volume
Specific Gravity	Unlimited
Reid Vapor Pressure	Between 5 and 7 pounds per square inch
Temperature	Between 425 and 600° F. (at end point) at the 90 percent evaporation point

Aviation gasoline might be said to be too highly refined for the comparatively modest requirements of aircraft jet powerplants. Kerosene has the advantage of higher heating value. The JP-1 and JP-3 jet-fuel specifications, which refer essentially to kerosene, require the ability to burn at temperatures as low as — 80° F. under atmospheric conditions prevalent at an altitude of 60,000 feet. These specifications also list adequate sea-level flammability limits.

Vapor loss is far less of a problem with jet fuels than with gasolines. However, "surging," or the tendency of violent boiling, then settling, and then repeated boiling at high altitudes, is a serious drawback of the kerosene-base jet fuels. Research workers are investigating this phenomenon.

Aviation gasoline, since it has less aromatic content than the kerosene jet fuels, should, theoretically at least, produce minimum carbon deposits. Since these carbon deposits are very detrimental to engine operation, the small aromatic content is an important advantage of the jet gasoline fuels.

Kerosene could well become a critical item, since its availability is limited. Therefore, combustion research is concerned with the substitution of metallic and other compounds for kerosene and for other conventional hydrocarbon fuels. These replacement products include fluorine compounds and alcohols as well as compounds of aluminum and boron bases. Boron hydride is an example of the second group. Research workers claim that metallic-base fuels would ultimately make possible combustion efficiencies many times the values available from the hydrocarbon fuels. Further developments in the field of nuclear energy will undoubtedly disclose unlimited possibilities for aircraft jet powerplant fuels.

JET ENGINE LUBRICANTS

Jet engines have distinctive lubrication problems: they do not lend themselves to fuel dilution as a means of viscosity reduced for low temperature operation; thrust loads are high, particularly on axial-compressor engines where they tend to cause seizure, scoring, and fatigue; soak-back of turbine blade heat when the engine is stationary (hence not being cooled) imposes high temperatures on the disc bearings.

Chapter 4

TURBOPROP AND PROPJET POWERPLANTS

COMPARISON WITH PURE JET UNITS

The propjet, also called turbopropjet or turboprop, is a variation of the basic turbojet unit in which a conventional aircraft propeller is mounted on the central turbine shaft. The gas turbine actuates the compressor and, in addition, rotates the propeller blades. This arrangement is an attempt to combine the desirable features of the turbojet powerplant and the aircraft propeller. As has already been stated, some turboprop powerplants function merely as gas turbines, developing shaft horsepower only and exerting no jet thrust. These, of course, cannot be considered as jet-propelled aircraft.

One of the unfavorable features of pure jet powerplants is the fact that maximum jet power can be attained only at maximum values of air speed—as has been mentioned previously. Conversely, the conventional reciprocating aircraft powerplant is so designed that it provides its maximum power for the take-off. With the pure jet powerplant, long take-off runs are necessary, with all its problems, including that of safety, attending the provision of take-off power under heavy load. Another disadvantage of jet powerplants is the excessively high fuel consumption, which is almost twice that of a

52

conventional reciprocating engine of equivalent performance. This second factor is reflected in a lower endurance range of the pure jet powerplant and in a lower payload, since much more fuel must be carried.

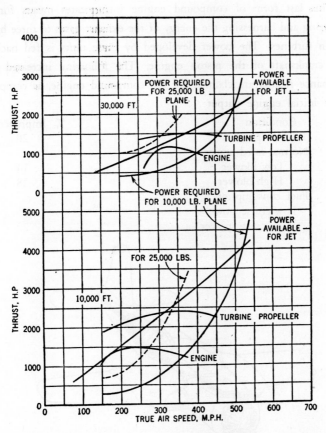

FIGURE 31. Composite Power Curves, Indicating Comparative Performance of Reciprocating Engines, Turbojet, and Propjet Powerplants.

THE COMPOUND POWERPLANT

The compound powerplant is designed to combine jet power with the fuel economy, increased range, and higher payload of a reciprocating engine. This assembly comprises a reciprocating aircraft engine operated in conjunction with a gas turbine. In some cases, it was contemplated to actuate the turbine unit with the exhaust gases of the reciprocating engine, since approximately 40 percent of the thermal energy of the main engine would still be available in the exhaust gases.

This last form of compound engine incorporates means for recovering and harnessing the energy of the exhaust gases to three blowdown turbines. The power developed by these units is fed back to the crankshaft of the piston engine. The following increased performance factors are claimed for the compound engine, as compared with initial engine output:

Condition	% Improvement
Take-off power	20
Normal rated power	
Low blower	14
High blower	28
Fuel consumption	
Low-cruise power	15
High-cruise power	20

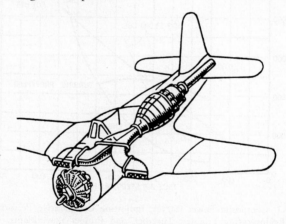

FIGURE 32. *An Example of the Compounding of Powerplants:* The Navy Ryan "Fireball" fighter with a reciprocating radial aircraft engine in addition to a General Electric "I-16" turbojet unit.

A limitation of the compound engine is the relatively low initial power available from the basic reciprocating powerplant. The maximum outputs predicted are in the 4,000 to 5,000 horsepower range, whereas turboprop powerplants of 10,000 to 20,000 horsepower output are envisioned for the immediate future.

FIGURE 33. The Principle of the Compound Powerplant.

One unusual compound engine incorporates two independent powerplants. This installation is employed on the Ryan "Fireball" Navy fighter airplane of figure 32. A reciprocating radial engine is mounted in front and a self-contained turbojet powerplant in the rear of the aircraft. The reciprocating engine is used for take-off and landing, as well as for maximum cruising economy. When additional power is required for acceleration, combat tactics, or high-altitude operation, the rear turbojet powerplant can be put into full operation within 12 seconds.

The turbojet powerplant, being completely isolated at the rear of the airplane, receives atmospheric air for combustion through ducts in the leading edge of the wing panels and on the nose section of the fuselage. The same fuel is fed for both powerplants, so that only one fuel-supply system is required.

FIGURE 34. The Wright "Turbo Cyclone" Compound Powerplant.

THE TURBOFAN

Another suggestion for the improvement of jet power at take-off is the ducted fan, or turbofan. This device consists of a bladed rotor, actuated by a secondary jet stream to supplement the thrust developed at take-off and at higher speeds of 400 to 500 miles per hour. The ducted-fan engine combines the economy of the turboprop powerplant

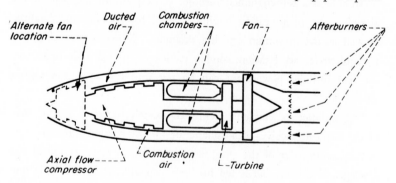

FIGURE 35. The Ducted Fan System.

with the high thrust of the turbojet powerplant. It offers, therefore, an interesting compromise between these two prominent forms of aircraft propulsion.

PERFORMANCE CHARACTERISTICS

Performance data of turbopropjet powerplants, measured under actual flight conditions, indicate that this unit yields take-off power, fuel economy, endurance range, and a payload potential comparable to those of the best conventional reciprocating engine at speeds below 350 miles per hour, and even superior performance within the range of 350 to 450 miles per hour and beyond.

At first glance, very little difference appears to exist between the internal-combustion turbine of the pure turbojet powerplant and the unit contemplated for installation in the turbopropjet powerplant, but for a slightly modified proportioning of the air compressor to the turbine. However, the compressor units and reduction gear boxes represent important differences in the turbopropjet powerplant. In some of the earlier turbopropjet models, reduction gear boxes were attached to existing turbojet-engine types. It was found that this arrangement caused engine unbalance and resulted, finally, in destructive vibrations.

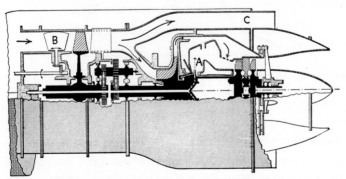

FIGURE 36. The Turbomeca Aspin Turbofan Engine.

Turbopropjet-powered aircraft function necessarily at lower operating speeds than does a turbojet-powered craft. Consequently, considerably larger compression ratios must be provided in the turbopropjet in order to supply equivalent pressure to the combustion chamber. This is necessary because the turbopropjet powerplant functions without the aid of the ram pressure which is available to the pure turbojet powerplant. The compression ratios can be increased by adding more stages of compression, by increasing the size of the compressor unit, or by improving the efficiency of the compressor. Any one of these solutions involves the addition of weight and of complex devices. The result is, however, well worth the effort, as the specific fuel consumption will be materially reduced by an increase in either the compression ratio or the compressor efficiency.

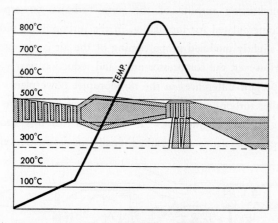

FIGURE 37. Temperature Gradient through a Typical Turboprop Powerplant.

Turbopropjet powerplants cannot be selected from the open market and adapted to a given airplane design, as are the piston-type engines. Aerodynamic factors, such as cruising speed and altitude, determine, to a great degree, the values of compression and thrust attainable by the turbopropjet unit. These design factors must be carefully coordinated before adapting the turbopropjet engine to a given airframe structure.

Favorable features of the turbopropjet are its high power output, low installation weight, and small frontal area. The last feature is responsible for the aerodynamically clean, "buried" installations which are characteristic of the high-performance, turbopropjet-powered aircraft beginning to roll off factory assembly lines.

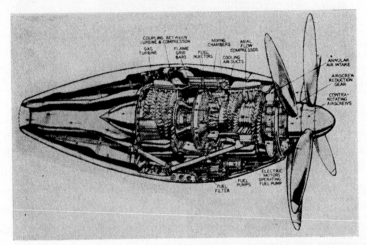

FIGURE 38. Layout of a Propjet Powerplant with Contrarotating Propellers.

The noise level of the turboproject powerplant is, in general, considerably below that of a piston engine of comparable performance. While the turbopropjet, as all forms of aircraft turbine engines, may not have the basic flexibility of the conventional piston powerplant, it offers a practically equivalent measure of operating flexibility in that one or more jet powerplants may be cut out during flight and operation continued at maximum revolutions per minute on the remaining jet units.

By suitable design modifications in the propeller reduction-gear assembly, provision can be made to accommodate contra-rotating propellers of highly efficient compensated torque characteristics.

The composite power curves of figure 31 give a comparison of the performance data of pure jet and turbopropjet powerplants, as well as of the conventional reciprocating engine.

FIGURE 39. Turboprop Powerplant (The General Electric "TG-100").

SUPERSONIC PROPELLERS

The addition of the conventional aircraft propeller to the turboprop-jet powerplant introduces the problems attending reduced propeller efficiency at high rotative velocities which have been mentioned in previous pages. The propeller research laboratories, however, contend that this situation is only an intermediate state of development and present a most optimistic outlook for the future. Supersonic propellers are reported to be in advanced planning, and even design, stages of development and awaiting only the anticipated high power

FIGURE 40. The British Armstrong Siddeley "Python" Turboprop Powerplant.

outputs from improved aircraft gas-turbine units to be transformed into a practical and efficient means of propulsion.

These propellers will be probably assembled of six or eight blades,

FIGURE 41. The USAF "C-97" Stratofreighter Fitted with Turboprops.

each 5 or 6 feet in diameter. These small diameters are proposed in order to permit better ground clearance. The multiple-blade arrangement expedites the handling of a greater air mass in order to secure a very high thrust force. Rotation velocities of 7,000 to 8,000 revolu-

FIGURE 42. The General Electric "TG-100" Turbopropjet on the Test Stand.

tions per minute are expected from the supersonic propeller. Spinner units will probably extend from the power shaft to approximately one-half the propeller-blade length to reduce the drag which builds up in the immediate region of the propeller hub.

The configuration of the supersonic propeller blade is contemplated to have the contour of a thin, triangular airfoil with sharp leading and trailing edges. The blade tips are envisioned as being swept back, much in the same manner as the blade of a Turkish scimitar. This departure from conventional practice becomes necessary because of possible compressibility effects, in view of the large air mass involved. The scimitar configuration will reduce the velocity of the air mass.

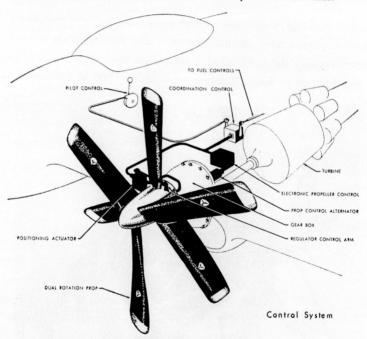

FIGURE 43. The "Aeroproducts" Turbine Engine Propeller.

THE JET-PROPELLED HELICOPTER

Although any conception of the jet-propelled helicopter would be only very distantly related to the principle of the turbopropjet powerplant, a brief reference will be made to this interesting application of jet propulsion. The helicopter lends itself admirably to the use of jet power. The drive applies the reaction principle to the helicopter rotor blades. An early design has a central turbojet powerplant, the so-called gas-stream unit, which supplies a constant stream of high-temperature fuel-air mixture to the hollow mounting member and hub of the helicopter rotor. From this point, the heated combustion gases pass, through channels in the interior of the blade, to an exit orifice located at the trailing edge of the blade tip. The hot gases, being ejected from the exit orifice, generate reactive thrust in the same manner as in jet-powered aircraft structures.

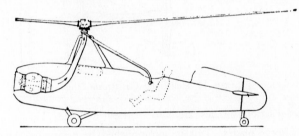

FIGURE 44. Jet-propelled Helicopter.

Since no mechanical drive of any kind is required for the helicopter rotor, this free-running characteristic should give the rotor member high stability. Therefore, control, when hovering or ascending vertically from ground levels, should be excellent.

A constant stream of high-temperature combustion gases is delivered to the blade extremities through a universal joint located at the central portion of the hub. Consequently, gastight construction of the universal joint is imperative. Additional gastight joints are needed to accommodate variable-pitch devices that are also incorporated in the lifting and directing rotor of the aircraft. Extreme smoothness is obtainable with the jet-propelled helicopter, since the revolutions of the rotor are constant and completely free from periodic fluctuations. Irrespective of the relative position of the aircraft and of the blade tip path, the blades are not subjected to "flapping" action with reference to the rotative member of the hub assembly. This desirable feature is a direct result of the free-turning rotor being driven from its periphery, rather than from the central hub. Another advantage of this arrangement is the nonexistence of centrifugal couples. The helicopter-airframe design is greatly simplified because no force couples are transmitted to it from the rotor member. Thus, only simple forces must be considered, i.e., the thrust along the axis of the blade-tip path, and a small down-wind force.

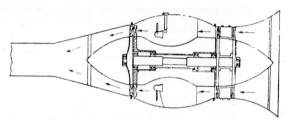

FIGURE 45. Helicopter Gas-stream Unit.

The jet-reaction nozzles are also utilized for mass balancing the helicopter rotor blades. This is accomplished by arranging the blade members in such a manner that the center of pressure of each individual blade is sufficiently close to its leading edge for the inertia, centrifugal, and aerodynamic forces to interact with one another, as well as with the elastic forces of the blade. In this manner, torsional twisting of the blade, with a consequent tendency to blade flutter, is opposed and prevented.

Icing of the helicopter rotor blades is automatically eliminated by the constant passage of the high-temperature combustion gases within these members.

The jet nozzle functions in conjunction with a thrust-augmentor device. The complete assembly consists of an outer chamber, incorporating a forward air intake located on the leading edge of the rotor blade and a venturi tube, facing to the rear. In operation, the jet ejector nozzle discharges gas into the throat section of the venturi tube.

The mass discharge of the heated combustion gases is thus augmented by the flow of the atmospheric air drawn in from the region immediately in front of the leading edge of the rotor blade.

Although the jet-propelled helicopter has rudder and elevator control surfaces of the conventional airplane type, a high degree of directional stability is provided by the rotor assembly.

More advanced jet-powered helicopter designs contain small pulsejet or ramjet units in the main rotor tips. In general, the pulsejet powerplant, when so employed, has proved to be less sensitive to rotor speed and yawing effect than its ramjet counterpart.

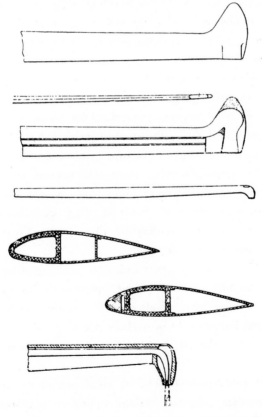

FIGURE 46. Structural Details of Jet-propelled Helicopter Blades.

The conventional long barrel of the resonance-tuned pulsejet is impractical for helicopter application because of the high induced centrifugal forces. Therefore, considerably shorter exhaust tubes, as small as 8 inches in some cases, are employed. In fact, all forms of rotortip aeroduct powerplants are small, one prominent design weighing only 10 pounds. Liquid propane serves as fuel, which is preheated prior to introduction into the powerplant. Exhaust stacks project upward and remove the combustion fumes from the crew area.

The use of an aeroduct powerplant for helicopter operation promises great advantages, with a view to the elimination of torque forces. This highly desirable feature will serve to eliminate the conventional heavy rotor-head forgings and fittings, as well as tail rotors. All these components are necessary in helicopter installations powered by reciprocating powerplants.

The undesirable factors include exposed flames, elevated noise level, and high fuel consumption, which may be serious obstacles to the widespread use of jet-propelled powerplants for this purpose. From the aspect of safety in flight, in the event of power failure, the aeroduct-engined helicopter assumes an excessive speed of descent due to auto-rotation. The ramjet powerplant is the chief offender in this respect. The pulsejet-powered helicopter, because of its somewhat superior ratio of "power-on" thrust to "power-off" drag, operates better under power-failure conditions. The difficulty is by no means insurmountable, but can be corrected by redesign.

It is significant that the ramjet helicopter has a useful load to gross weight ratio as high as 70. This value represents the highest lift ratio attained by existing types of aircraft. This factor, coupled with its simplicity and improved flying qualities due to greatly increased moment of inertia, make the ramjet helicopter a great promise of the future.

A further application involves the installation of turbojet powerplants in standard helicopter designs to provide additional take-off and landing thrust. The British Fairey "Rotodyne" is an example of this type of arrangement. In the United States, the Howard Hughes "XH-17," called the "flying crane," has two separate "J-35" turbojet powerplants. This is a huge craft, the span of the two-bladed rotor being 136 feet.

The jet-powered "convertaplane" is a very recent experimental project. It consists, essentially, of a jet-rotored autogyro, but the rotor is utilized only for ascent and descent and not for level flight.

OPERATIONAL LIMITATIONS OF TURBOPROP
POWERPLANTS

Single-engine turboprop failure on takeoff or landing approach induces severe drag conditions and loss of longitudinal control that permit insufficient time for recovery. Multi-engined turboprop installations encounter considerably more severe directional and lateral control requirements on engine failure than those of conventional piston-engined aircraft.

Control of thrust for the approach condition is difficult because of the extremely low propeller blade angle required to absorb the high idle speed of the turbine powerplant.

Thrust is subject to wide variation because of fluctuations in fuel flow, induced, in turn, by compressor bleeds and accessory load variations.

Chapter 5

THE ROCKETJET POWERPLANT

The Rocket a Self-sustained Unit

Although the rocket is still classified primarily as a guided missile rather than as an aircraft powerplant, a detailed study of this form of power development will not be amiss. In a few isolated cases, rocket-propelled aircraft has been more or less successfully tested in flight and there is a fair chance that rocket power will invade the realm of conventional aircraft powerplants at some future time.

We may classify the rocket, for the purpose of this book, as a jet-propelled aircraft which differs from the pure jet powerplants that were previously considered only in that it transports the oxygen supply essential for the complete combustion of its fuel within its main structure. This makes the rocket-type craft a completely independent and self-sustaining unit, which does not need atmospheric air for combustion.

The rightful province of the rocket is the super-stratosphere, altitudes of the order of 10 or 15 miles and far beyond, where air-burning powerplants, whether reciprocating, turbojet, or aeroduct, would fail or "starve" from lack of atmospheric oxygen. It is not within the scope of this text to investigate the rocket, either its function as a guided missile, or as a medium with which to explore the mysteries of interstellar space. It should be noted only that the rocket represents one of the highest-output heat powerplants known in its weight group. To select a typical example, one form of rocket powerplant of German origin, the "V-2," weighs 12 tons, 9 tons of which is oxygen and alcohol utilized as fuel. This unit exerts 58,000 pounds of thrust when launched at take-off. The weight of the rocket is reduced rapidly, since fuel is consumed at the rate of 260 pounds per second. Combustion occurs at temperatures of the order of 7,000° F., the resultant jet of heated combustion gases attaining a velocity of approximately 6,400 feet per second. As the craft tends to accelerate up to a forward velocity of 3,500 miles per hour, the power output is 600,000 horsepower. Thus, approximately 16 horsepower is produced for each pound of the craft's weight. This figure is surpassed only by the output of the ramjet powerplant, which, as mentioned before, can produce the equivalent of 1 horsepower for each ½ ounce of its total weight.

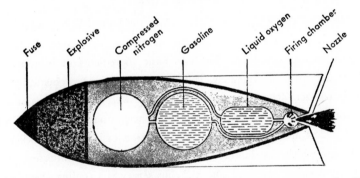

FIGURE 47. *Diagram of a Rocketjet Powerplant:* The gasoline and self-contained liquid oxygen are forced into the combustion chamber under pressure of nitrogen gas.

SOLID AND LIQUID FUELS

Basically, rocketjets can operate with both dry and liquid fuels. In either case, the craft contains all of the elements essential for complete combustion. In the dry-fueled rocketjet, a slow-burning powder is employed which incorporates the oxygen required for complete combustion. An initial limitation of dry fuels is their lack of controllability. Powder rocketjet fuels, once ignited, burn completely and then the thrust ceases. Liquid-fueled rocketjets utilize liquefied oxygen, e.g., with gasoline or alcohol. Liquid oxygen is the most concentrated form of oxygen available. It is manufactured by liquefying atmospheric air and boiling off the nitrogen and other gases contained in it. In many cases, an inert gas, such as nitrogen, is used to force the fuel into the combustion chamber under pressure.

FIGURE 48. Rocketjet Powerplant Configurations.

MONOPROPELLANTS AND BIPROPELLANTS

Other widely used rocket fuels include the bipropellant combination of nitric acid and aniline, and the somewhat more compact monopropellant, nitromethane. The two basic ingredients of bipropellant fuels are injected separately, combustion occurring automatically on their contact. The cooling of rocketjet powerplants is a major engineering problem in view of the high-energy fuels employed. Cooling jackets are constructed integral with the casing of the rocketjet, through which the liquid fuel is circulated prior to injecting into the combustion chamber. The fuel thus serves as a cooling agent, and, is some cases, is vaporized at the high temperatures to which the rocketjet casings are subjected.

SELECTION OF FUELS

In general, two considerations of vital importance govern the selection of rocketjet fuels. The first factor is designated as specific impulse and represents essentially the pounds of thrust developed per pound of fuel burned per second. An equally vital second factor is the density, or weight per unit volume, of the fuel. A mixture composed of 80 percent liquid hydrogen and 20 percent liquid oxygen produces the highest specific impulse available, i.e., roughly 350 seconds. Liquid oxygen, when burned in immediate proximity of a liquid hydrocarbon, liberates about 50 percent more heat than nitric acid or peroxide fuels. However, the losses of liquid oxygen by dissociation and vaporization are higher than those of nitric acid and peroxide fuels.

In actual operation, the aggregate heat loss of liquid oxygen is practically 50 percent, which approximates twice that of the nitric acid fuels and four times that of peroxide.

Nitric acid, utilized as a source of oxygen supply for rocketjet powerplants, offers, in addition to its favorable heat energy properties, the following advantages: low vapor pressure; wide availability; advantageous freezing point; stability; and, good storage and transportation properties. The destructively corrosive character of nitric acid can be entirely eliminated by using it in highly concentrated form only and by storing nitric acid fuels in moistureproof containers. The toxic properties of nitrogen dioxide can also be ignored, as this gas is formed only at comparatively low temperatures and thus its formation can be avoided. In operation, the nitric acid fuel does not require an ignition system, because it ignites spontaneously, which reduces the weight and simplifies the design of the powerplant.

Several other chemical fuel combinations have desirable features. One of them, diborane-oxygen, has produced phenomenal combustion temperatures in the 6,800° F. range. Some of the newer fuels have greater values of specific impulse than the liquid oxygen-hydrogen combination. However, the majority of these fuels is in an experimental stage and is not commercially available. The following chemical rocketjet fuels are arranged in the order of their over-all effectiveness.

> Gasoline-acid
>
> Alcohol-oxygen

Hydrazine-chlorine-fluorine

Diborane-oxygen

Diborane-fluorine

Hydrogen-oxygen

Hydrogen-fluorine

The dangers involved in handling these fuels will undoubtedly prevent their acceptance or, at least, their widespread use. The principal offenders in this respect are the hydrogen-oxygen and hydrogen-fluorine combinations.

Hydrogen peroxide still retains an outstanding position as a rocket-engine fuel, because it is readily available in commercial quantities, it has high density, high specific energy release, and a high percentage of available oxygen. It is reasonably stable in extended storage and has a negative heat of formation. Hydrogen peroxide performs best in the presence of a suitable catalyst, potassium permanganate or potassium cuprocyanide being used for this purpose. Foreign rocketjets use hydrogen peroxide with gasoline or hydrazine hydrate and report excellent results.

An oxidizer, as distinguished from an actual rocketjet fuel, is an agent which supports combustion at high altitudes. Nitrogen tetroxide is widely used for this purpose. It is manufactured from ammonia. Its chemical stability, high density, and low freezing point make it very suitable for use in rocketjet powerplants.

DISADVANTAGES OF ROCKETJET POWERPLANTS

Two particularly disadvantageous properties of rocketjet operation are the so-called "chugging" and the ignition delay. The first term designates the fluctuations in the firing of rocket fuels. In extreme cases, the flame expires in the combustion chamber only to flare out (at a constant frequency) in a long trail rearward of the rocketjet powerplant. The second undesirable feature is a short delay in the ignition of the rocket charge. Although, this delay is only a few hundreths of a second, it is still sufficient to operate highly volatile rocket fuel to accumulate in the combustion chamber and then to create a violent explosion when the actual ignition occurs. Both of these drawbacks can be corrected. Suggested remedies included the preheating of the fuel and the addition of suitable substances which slow down the combustion.

Recent research is concentrated on the development of some form of intermittent rocket action. This arrangement would extend to a limited range of rocketjets. It is quite possible that the nitric acid fuels, with certain additives, such as iron trichloride, will introduce sufficient ignition delay to provide for the ideal condition.

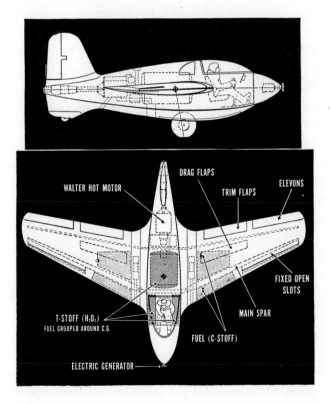

FIGURE 49. The German Messerschmitt "ME-163B" Rocketjet Fighter Aircraft.

The Messerschmitt "ME-163" Aircraft

There are two pioneer, pilot-controlled aircraft, powered by rocket-jet powerplants which function entirely as prime movers. Both are of foreign manufacture: the Messerschmitt "ME-163" is of German origin; the other is the Japanese "Baka" of Kamikaze memory.

The Messerschmitt ME-163 comprises a single-seat, mid-wing monoplane which looks like an arrowhead in plan view. The wing panels have a sharp sweepback, that of the leading edge being considerably more pronounced than that of the trailing edge. The short fuselage is formed in streamlined "tear-drop" contour and is unusually deep in relation to its comparatively short length. The control surfaces consist of a single vertical fin and rudder, the absence of the conventional horizontal stabilizer and elevator combination being conspicuous. The cockpit, with its jettisonable canopy, is faired smoothly into the fuselage contour. A small-diameter propeller, which actuates a generator for instrument operation, is mounted on the nose section. The inboard wing sections are made of wood and fabric, while the nose and wing tips are made of metal. A landing-gear assembly is used for take-off only and is subsequently jettisoned. Landings are accomplished on a fuselage skid, 8 inches in width, which is supplemented by a small tail skid. The proportional dimensions of the ME-163 are as follows:

Wing span: 30 feet   Total weight (normal load), 11,500 pounds
                      Total wing area, 220 square feet
Length: 20 feet   Wing loading (normal load), 52 pounds per
                      square foot

There are two variations of the ME-163 rocketjet powerplant, widely differing in their fuels. One modification of the aircraft, apparently contemplated for use as a trainer craft, contained a "cold" single-liquid rocket-propulsion unit, while the tactical version of the ME-163 was powered by a "hot" unit. In either case, the fuels consisted of two basic ingredients: a propellant and an igniter, and interaction of these two elements produced the combustion.

Hot and Cold Rocket Units

A "cold" unit is a rocketjet powerplant which utilizes a hydrogen peroxide base fuel, to which a relatively small amount of methyl alcohol is added. A potassium permanganate solution serves as a catalyst which accelerates the reaction between the two basic ingredients of the fuel. It is called "cold" unit because it can be operated at a comparatively low temperature. The long vaporization trail attending the flight of this type of rocketjet powerplant is characteristic of the low operating temperature.

The "hot" rocketjet powerplant is associated with dense exhaust flames, up to 50 feet in length, ejected from the jet orifice. The overall efficiency of the rocketjet powerplant is improved by increasing the combustion temperature through the utilization of more concentrated fuel. Considerably greater fire hazard attends the operation of the "hot" unit, particularly when it is started prior to actual flight. Both types of power units develop a specific thrust of 180 pounds and a maximum thrust of approximately 3,000 pounds in the case of the ME-163.

One previously mentioned disadvantage of the rocketjet powerplant is its high fuel consumption. The fuel load represents a very large proportion of the total aircraft weight. Consequently, the fuel load must be accommodated in such a manner within the structure of the aircraft that no appreciable change in the location of the center of gravity occurs as the fuel is consumed and thus the weight of the airplane is considerably reduced. The sweepback of the wing panels affects the center of lift, and, in so doing, greatly facilitates the disposal of a large fuel load in the rear section of the fuselage. A space of 100 cubic feet is provided which can hold 748 U.S. gallons of fuel.

The total weight, including the main fuel load and the catalyst, is 11,500 pounds. The total wing area being 220 square feet, the wing loading is approximately 52 pounds per square foot.

In evaluating the performance of the ME-163, its air speed has been determined to be 500 to 600 miles per hour. The craft can maintain extremely high speeds in prolonged steep climb. Opposition aircraft were unable to follow the ME-163 in very steep dives. The air-speed indicators of the ME-163 were found to be calibrated to a miximum speed of 992 miles per hour. The rocketjet powerplant can be brought from gliding flight to full-power flight within 10 seconds.

The full power endurance of the ME-163 is 8 to 12 minutes. However, when using the rocketjet powerplant intermittently, the fuel weight is considerably reduced, with the craft assuming the characteristics of a glider. Then, the aircraft is able to cruise for a considerable length of time, 2¾ hours according to some reports, with very little loss in altitude. When the fuel load is completely expended, the wing loading of the craft is 14 pounds per square foot.

Although the ME-163 allegedly can take off without assistance, it normally employs a 1,000 yard runway, fitted with rails to be used with rocket-assist devices. This arrangement is utilized to conserve fuel. Where prolonged endurance was called for, a fuel overload necessitated the use of more than 3,000-yard-long runways.

The initial rate of climb with normal load is 5,000 feet per minute at sea level, and 10,000 feet per minute at 40,000 feet. The rapid decrease of weight accompanying the high fuel consumption is a contributory factor to this high performance at higher altitude.

The Russian "Yak-21" is a direct adaptation of the ME-163B, powered by the "hot" Walter rocketjet motor. Approximately 3,500 pounds of thrust is available from the improved powerplant. Fuel is consumed at the rate of 1,100 pounds per minute. Russian designers have added a tail plane to the original ME-163B model. This member controls nose-down pitching tendencies which occur at high subsonic Mach numbers.

THE "BAKA" ROCKET-POWERED AIRCRAFT

The author had the opportunity of investigating a captured Japanese "Baka" rocketjet aircraft while on the island of Okinawa. Although very aptly designated as a pilot-controlled flying bomb, the Baka has

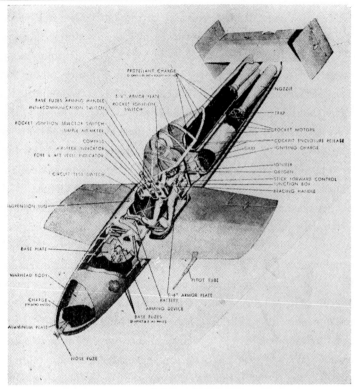

FIGURE 50. Japanese "Baka" Rocket-powered Aircraft.

all the characteristics of the conventional airplane. There is provision for its being launched from a "mother" aircraft while in flight. The Baka is attached to the bomb bay of the larger aircraft by means of a single mounting lug and a system of slings fastened under the wings and empennage.

The structural and performance specifications of the Baka aircraft are as follows:

Wing span   16 feet 5 inches   Maximum air speed (level
Length   19 feet 10 inches   flight) 535 miles per hour
Weight   4,537 pounds   Maximum range 55 miles
                        Maximum height (depth
                        of fuselage) 31 feet 10¼ inches

The main wing panels, as well as the horizontal and vertical stabilizers, are made of wood, while the fuselage is entirely fabricated of metal. All control surfaces are equipped with dynamic balance devices, the function of which is to minimize flutter at the high values of forward velocity at which the craft is contemplated to operate. No landing gear of any kind is provided.

Five separate rocketjet powerplants propel the Baka aircraft. Six grains of propellant are provided for each rocket-jet unit. With three of the power units operating in unison, sufficient thrust is developed to maintain powered flight for a distance of 3 miles. Three of the rocketjet powerplants are mounted in the rear-tail cone, the remaining two units being beneath the wing panels. The propellant charges in the units can be fired either individually or simultaneously, at the discretion of the pilot. The control system comprises a conventional stick and rudder yoke arrangement. Other control facilities include a selector switch for firing the rocket propulsion charges and a pull-type arming handle for actuating the base fuses of the explosive charge carried by the aircraft. The few instruments provided include a compass and deviation card, an altimeter, an airspeed indicator calibrated up to 600 knots, an inclinometer, a turn and bank indicator, a card holder, and a circuit test switch. Communication facilities are also provided and consist of an intercommunication switch, lights, and an air horn. By means of these devices, the pilot can communicate with the crew of the "mother" aircraft. A small oxygen bottle, the capacity of which permits approximately ½ hour of operation at 20,000 feet, is also made available to the pilot.

One-third of the Baka aircraft is devoted to the war head, that is why it is called "flying bomb." This front portion of the fuselage carries the explosive charge which is completely covered by a streamlined fairing. The complete war head weighs 2,645 pounds. The explosive charge proper weighs 1,135 pounds and consists of trinitroanisol. Five fuses are incorporated in the warhead section, one being located on the nose and the remaining four on the base. The nose fuse is a straight impact fuse and is vane-armed. Two of the base fuses are of the impact type, the other two being of the "all way" type. All four base fuses can be armed manually from the cockpit of the aircraft. A post and ring sight is mounted on the nose section and assists the pilot in aiming the Baka aircraft at its target.

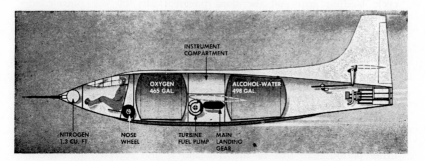

FIGURE 51. The Bell "X-1" Rocketjet Research Aircraft.

THE BELL RESEARCH AIRCRAFT

The Bell Aircraft Corporation of Buffalo, New York, has developed the "X-1," a supersonic, alcohol-fueled rocketjet aircraft. This unit has been recently tested in flight with great success. Designed for a maximum performance of Mach 1.18 (118 percent of the speed of sound, as we have already explained), the "X-1" primarily serves as a flying laboratory. The attainment of Mach 2 at 30,000 feet and approximately 1,350 miles per hour could reasonably be anticipated with this aircraft. Although totaling 12,000 pounds gross weight, when launched from its B-29 "mother" aircraft, the "X-1" lands at 7,000 pounds. This weight reduction is a result of the very high fuel consumption. The 30-foot span aircraft structure is stressed for values of acceleration as high as 18 G's, in order to withstand the buffeting from compression at the threshold of the sonic barrier, and, possibly, beyond. The X-1 is powered by four rocketjet powerplants, designed and manufactured by Reaction Motors, Inc., producing a total of 6,000 pounds thrust. The liquid oxygen and alcohol propellants burn at 5000° Rankine, this excessive temperature necessitating regenerative cooling of the combustion chambers. This procedure involves circulation of the alcohol constituent of the fuel through cooling jackets surrounding the combustion chambers prior to injecting into the combustion chamber. A special feature of the X-1 is the operation of the retractable tricycle landing gear and the flaps pneumatically by the pressurized nitrogen supply.

An improved version, the Bell X-2, is powered by Curtiss-Wright rocketjet engines, developing a total output of 15,000 pounds thrust. The thrust is so distributed that 10,000 pounds are delivered from one cylinder and 5,000 pounds from another cylinder. The fuel tanks under nitrogen pressure have been modified to accommodate a turbo fuel-feed pump. The introduction of this pump permits a longer firing period than that of the X-1 and is also reflected in reduced over-all weight of the powerplant.

A still newer version, the X-5 is a needle-nose research aircraft. It is powered by a single Allison J-35-A-17, and is thus not a rocketjet aircraft. It is mentioned here briefly and only because of its two predecessors. An unusual feature is the electrically-operated variable-sweep wing. As the sweepback is varied, the wings move forward along the fuselage. For take-off and climb, the straight-wing configuration is preferable. For bridging transsonic speeds, the sweepback can be increased to a maximum value of over 50°.

FIGURE 52. Reaction Motors, Incorporated's Model 6000-C4, Four-Cylinder, Regeneratively-cooled Rocketjet Powerplant.

FIGURE 53. Reaction Motors, Incorporated's Rocketjet Powerplant on Test Stand.

JATO

A further application of rocket power in aeronautics is the rocket-assisted take-off. This innovation, also known as "JATO," (meaning "jet-assisted take-off"), can be installed on any existing aircraft. Reductions up to 60 percent in take-off run requirements have been effected by JATO.

JATO rocket powerplants resemble large steel bottles. They are employed in batteries of two to four units, and are mounted on either side of the hull or fuselage of the aircraft. They are auxiliary powerplants, supplementing the output of the main engines of the aircraft in order to furnish the high power required for the take-off. The fuel is a solid propellant containing the oxygen essential for complete combustion. The rocket charge is ignited by means of an electrical firing circuit, manually controlled by the pilot. A thrust force of approximately 300 equivalent horsepower is developed by an individual rocket unit, when producing its maximum power output. As soon as the take-off is safely accomplished and the aircraft is air borne, the burned-out rocket casings can be jettisoned. The aircraft is then operated solely by its main engines.

FIGURE 54. A Jet-assisted Takeoff.

One prominent form of rocket powerplant, designed for JATO application, is manufactured by the Aerojet Engineering Corporation. This unit comprises a seamless steel cylinder, 10 inches in diameter and 3 feet in length. The forward extremity of the casing is closed. Provision is made on the rear end of the casing for the installation of the rocketjet nozzle, the ignition device, and a safety blow-out device. The nozzle throat is fitted with a carbon insert to protect the nozzle from the effects of erosion at high temperatures. Three mounting lugs are welded to the exterior of the rocketjet casing. The total weight of the powerplant is 115 pounds, of which the cartridge containing the solid propellant weighs 90 pounds. The propellant ignites at 725° F. At take-off velocities of the order of 90 miles per hour, the rocketjet exerts a thrust force of approximately 330 equivalent horsepower.

In operation of the JATO powerplant, the electrical ignition circuit actuates a flash cap when closed by the pilot. This activates the main charge, which, in turn, ignites the propellant. Approximately 0.2 second suffices for the entire series of events to occur.

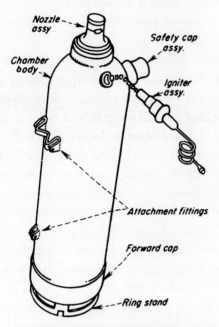

FIGURE 55. The JATO Catridge Motor Manufactured by Aerojet Engineering Corporation.

To evaluate the take-off performance of a conventional aircraft equipped with a JATO unit, a hypothetical twin-engined transport airplane of 25,000 pounds gross weight will be briefly analyzed. Civil Aeronautics Authority requirements allot this type of aircraft a take-off run distance of 4,000 feet under normal conditions, without any form of take-off assistance. However, when auxiliary rocket power is introduced, after approximately 920 feet of sea-level runway travel, the aircraft becomes air borne within 1,660 feet. Furthermore, a 50-foot obstacle can be readily cleared with one engine operative within 2,587 feet. In a locality situated 4,800 feet above sea level, rocket assist power, when introduced after 1,115 feet of runway travel, causes the same type of aircraft to become air borne after a total take-off run of 2,193 feet. Under these conditions, a 50-foot obstacle can be cleared, following a run of 3,261 feet. This performance becomes still more impressive when it is considered that this type of aircraft, operating in a locality of 4,800 feet elevation, requires a run of 5,500 feet for single-engine take-off.

The performance data for most types of aircraft are predicated on the requirements for cruising air speeds approximately 40 to 50 miles per hour in excess of the normal take-off velocity. Under these conditions, a fatal accident can reasonably be anticipated if one engine fails during the critical period between the actual take-off and the attainment of minimum safe single-engine speed. The identical airplane, when equipped with an auxiliary rocket powerplant, would be able to proceed and accelerate to safe single-engine flying speed, should one engine become inoperative. Similarly, single-engined aircraft can be relieved of the hazards of take-off by the provision of auxiliary rocket power. Should the single engine become inoperative for any reason during the take-off period, the JATO power, even with its endurance limitations of 25 seconds, would permit the pilot to return to the airport of origin. Should the single engine become inoperative at cruising altitudes, the auxiliary rocketjet powerplant could be utilized to extend the glide sufficiently for the pilot to locate and reach a safe landing area. Gliders and sailplanes could be designed to incorporate auxiliary rocketjet powerplants. Then their rate of climb could approximate 3,000 feet per minute, easily attaining soaring altitudes within the endurance period of the rocketjet powerplant.

RATO

The term RATO is relatively new and refers specifically to rocket-assisted take-off, as distinguished from such jet-assisted take-off applications as liquid injection or afterburner assistance. Actually, the term RATO refers to liquid-propellant take-off devices, rather than to the solid-propellant take-off devices with which the original JATO was primarily associated.

Chapter 6

MAINTENANCE CONSIDERATIONS

Parts Serviceability

The general scope of aircraft powerplant maintenance, whether it concerns the conventional reciprocating engine, the pure jet powerplant, or the rocketjet, has two principal aspects: (1) parts serviceability, and (2) the determination of the level of maintenance required. These two factors are inseparable and both must be constantly considered to provide adequate maintenance.

Parts serviceability is maintained by a general survey of the fundamental operations which require periodic maintenance of the operating parts. There are three basic categories of trouble sources: dirt, heat, and motion.

The combustion chamber is normally the primary source of dirt in any type of heat engine. Heat is also dependent, in the first place, on the combustion chamber. In the jet powerplant, the combustion chamber is a thin-walled tubular section which is readily accessible and has a removable liner. The structural properties of the thin-walled section and the sustained elevated temperatures to which it is subjected make the replacement rate of the combustion-chamber members high.

A brief survey of turbojet powerplant layout will indicate that

FIGURE 56. The German "Jumo 004" Jet Powerplant, Powering the Messerschmitt "262" Fighter, Mounted on an American Test Stand.

dirt and heat are also closely associated with the operation of the turbine-rotor assembly. Thus, it is obvious that the turbine rotor will require frequent replacement.

The third basic cause of maintenance difficulties has been classified as motion, which is obtained by transformation of the thermal energy of the fuel into mechanical energy. The main source of motion is the turbine-rotor assembly which contains a central power shaft, carrying the compressor impeller and the turbine rotor. The high rotation velocity of this assembly and the elevated temperature of the

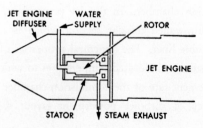

FIGURE 57. Vaporization-cooled Jet Powerplant Alternator.

combustion gases, with which it comes into direct contact, make necessary the frequent replacement of parts and, also, much rework. Another requirement is a perfect balance of the turbine rotor while in its assembled state. This necessitates disassembly prior to reinstallation in the powerplant casing, and then reassembly with all attaching nuts and bolts in their former relative positions in order to retain the balance. This procedure limits the useful life of the rotor and its components. After a predetermined number of balancing operations, the turbine-rotor members must be replaced.

DETERMINATION OF REQUIRED MAINTENANCE LEVELS

The determination of the requisite levels of maintenance for certain components entails careful study of the construction of these components and their behavior under operating conditions. The methods of maintenance inspections and their frequency will be based on this study.

For example, in certain turbojet powerplant subassemblies, disassembling involves removal of the retaining bolts through a system of flanged couplings. This maintenance function is required every 40 to 50 flying hours. However, it is a relatively simple procedure since, in addition to the bolts, only the turbine-nozzle assembly must be removed. Although the turbine-nozzle assembly can be removed and replaced as a complete unit, several metering devices must be used after reassembly. For this reason, disassembly and subsequent overhaul necessitates the facilities of an adequately equipped overhaul shop and cannot be carried out as a field maintenance project. However, field-maintenance facilities should be entirely adequate for drawing reassembled turbine nozzles from a stock of serviceable units and installing them on aircraft.

Another pertinent example is the removal of the turbine rotor which can be accomplished only through the progressive disassembly of a complete rotor group. Since the reassembly cannot be accomplished in the field, because balancing is required, the level of maintenance necessitated in this case is obviously that of an overhaul or repair depot.

Once a definite policy has been established on the level of maintenance required for each individual component and assembly, an index on the experience level of maintenance personnel can be set up and, if necessary, courses may be given through which the maintenance men may acquire additional knowledge.

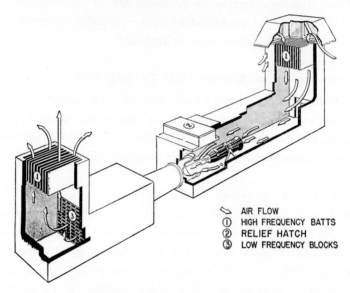

AIR FLOW
① HIGH FREQUENCY BATTS
② RELIEF HATCH
③ LOW FREQUENCY BLOCKS

FIGURE 58. Jet-engine Test Stand Layout.

COMPARISON WITH RECIPROCATING-ENGINE MAINTENANCE

One known design of turbojet powerplant can be removed from its mount in 20 minutes by a crew of experienced engine mechanics. There are only eleven small bolts to remove, so that even an inexperienced crew can do the work in 35 minutes. A crew of four trained mechanics can remove and fully reinstall two complete turbojet powerplants of this type in a single working day. Corresponding work on a conventional reciprocating engine would require about 5 days. Overhaul is also simplified, as the aircraft jet powerplant consists primarily of a casing, two main rotors, and the central power shaft.

FIGURE 59. J-33 Centrifugal-flow Turbojet on Its Mounting Stand.

In a newer, improved version of turbojet, the single unit can be removed from the airframe in 15 minutes. It is obvious that a complete engine change, involving both the removal and reinstallation of the jet powerplant, will require proportionately more time. By comparison, 16 man hours are required for the complete change of one piston engine of equivalent output rating in a conventional type of twin-engined airplane.

SIMPLIFIED MAINTENANCE OF JET POWERPLANTS

Another favorable aspect of jet-powerplant change is the small amount of equipment required. In jet-propelled aircraft, incorporating multiple outboard powerplant units, a small wing hoist and a frame are all the equipment needed. These can be transported in the airplane. A suitable cradle for holding the powerplant, when removed, is an essential item of field equipment.

Due to the underslung construction of jet-powered aircraft, the powerplant must be lowered 2 feet or so in a straight line to ground level. With a view to the low center of gravity of jet aircraft, no

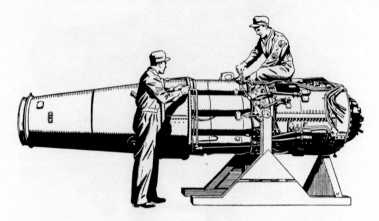

FIGURE 60. Axial-flow Turbojet Powerplant on Its Work Stand.

crew chief work stands, large-capacity hoists, and powered equipment are needed. The conventional wheeled "creeper" to accommodate mechanics when working in the prone position is essential for jet-powerplant maintenance.

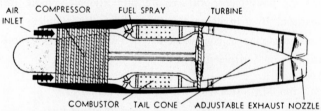

FIGURE 61. Adjustable Exhaust Nozzle on Turbojet Powerplant.

In contrast to the extensive systems of connections and leads common to the reciprocating aircraft engines, the jet-powerplant assembly incorporates only fuel lines, oil lines, tachometer and generator leads, and two thermocouple leads. One thermocouple lead extends back to the tail pipe and the other to the main-shaft bearing. The throttle is the sole engine control provided; it controls the amount of fuel injected into the burners. This determines the revolutions per minute of the engine and thus the forward velocity of the aircraft. In some cases, the throttle is a cone-shaped restriction which slides along the longitudinal axis of the tailpipe and varies the size of the jet exit orifice. In newer designs, hydraulically operated "eyelids," or partial enclosures at the exhaust end of the afterburner, can be opened to offer greater exhaust area. When the afterburner is cut out, the "eyelids" are closed to reduce the exhaust area.

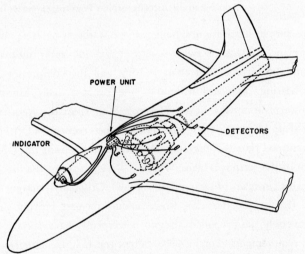

FIGURE 62. Fire-detection System Installed on a Turbojet-powered Aircraft.

The simplicity of the aircraft jet powerplant is also reflected in the small amount of working tools required for its maintenance. Only about one-fifth the amount of tools is required as are needed for maintenance of a reciprocating aircraft engine of equivalent output. In other words, where engine mechanics would normally utilize, say, twenty-five wrenches in maintaining a reciprocating engine, only five wrenches would be required for a similar operation on an aircraft jet powerplant.

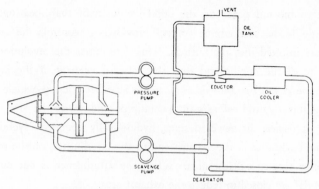

FIGURE 63. Closed-circuit Lubrication System
Applied to an Aircraft-turbine Powerplant.

The simple lubrication system, which, at the same time, cools the powerplant, consists of two oil jets. These jets spray lubricant and air into the turbine-rotor shaft bearing and the compressor-impeller shaft bearing. Standard hydraulic fluid could actually lubricate the jet powerplant satisfactorily. The excess oil from the rotor and impeller-shaft bearings flows into the accessory section and from there, it is returned by a scavenge pump. A cuno filter cleans the lubrication system of the jet powerplant. There is a trend toward the use of solid lubricants instead of the oil-air spray. Originally, designers were afraid that a solid lubricant would unduly increase bearing pressures.

Conversely, jet-propelled aircraft powerplants have special maintenance requirements. For instance, burner-can failures occur frequently; the can cracks or buckles. Badly heat-distorted cans require replacement. Preventive measures involve, primarily, some form of redesign. For example, some means of cooling the metal skin of the burner cans by air bleed can be provided. An alternate measure is the provision of an insulating coating in the interior of the cans. Both of these measures are now in use. As a direct result, jet-engine burner cans usually give a minimum of 200 hours of trouble-free service. Several instances of 400-hour operation have also been recorded.

The failure of nozzle guide vanes is also quite frequent, mainly

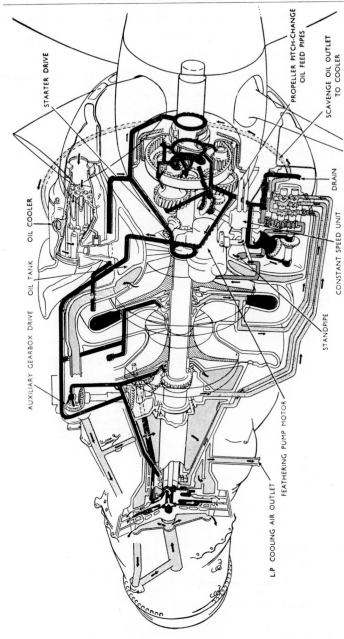

STARTER DRIVE

PROPELLER PITCH-CHANGE OIL FEED PIPES

SCAVENGE OIL OUTLET TO COOLER

DRAIN

CONSTANT SPEED UNIT

STANDPIPE

OIL COOLER

OIL TANK

AUXILIARY GEARBOX DRIVE

FEATHERING PUMP MOTOR

L.P COOLING AIR OUTLET

FIGURE 64. Lubrication System of the Rolls Royce "Dart" Turboprop Powerplant.

because of temperature variation and the accumulation of foreign material. Design progress tends to minimize vane failures. Of particular interest is the introduction of hollow vanes of uniform cross section, which have improved resistance to thermal shock. Controlled operation can also lengthen the life of the nozzle guide vane. This, however, would result in some performance loss as it would increase the specific fuel consumption and decrease the power output.

The fouling of engine flow paths is another jet-engine maintenance problem. This difficulty appears most frequently in the axial-flow turbine powerplants. So far, no satisfactory system has been devised for cleaning the flow paths during operation.

At present, overhaul of aircraft turbine engines is required for about 500 hours of operation. It appears reasonable to anticipate an engine life of 2,000 hours, or a span of four overhaul periods. This figure will be extended undoubtedly as design and operational know how progresses.

The cost of turbine-engine unit parts compares rather favorably with that of reciprocating powerplants. As the mass production of aircraft jet powerplants gains momentum, the cost may be expected

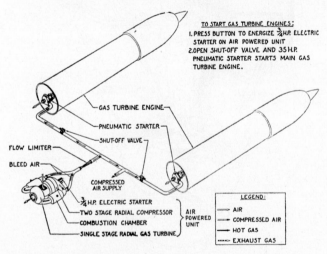

FIGURE 65. Starting System for Aircraft Gas-turbine Powerplants.

to be even lower. The high degree of parts interchangeability in the newer models of jet engines will greatly simplify the maintenance and reduce its cost.

MAINTENANCE OF JET POWERPLANT ACCESSORIES

The maintenance of jet powerplant accessory units is much easier than that of reciprocating engine accessories, because, for the operation of jet units, only a generator, a fuel pump, and a starter are needed. In typical jet-powered installations, the battery provided is of considerably smaller capacity than that employed in conventional aircraft. The generator must be maintained operative throughout the flight, as failure to actuate the generator switch would result in a run-down battery, which, in turn, would cause a failure of the instruments, radio-communication, and landing-gear systems.

Spark plugs are expected to have a short life span at the elevated temperatures of operation. Actually, however, they work about the same length of time as in a conventional reciprocating engine. The electrode gap is made considerably wider in spark plugs for use with jet powerplants. A single spark plug is required for aero-duct powerplants and two suffice for the operation of the majority of turbojet powerplants. In the case of centrifugal-flow units, employing multiple combustion chambers, all of the thin-walled chambers are interconnected and are ignited from the two chambers which are equipped with spark plugs.

MAINTENANCE OF JET POWERPLANT INSTRUMENTS

The maintenance of jet powerplant instruments is also simpler than in the regular aircraft. The jet-powered aircraft has no manifold pressure gage. The power output is calibrated with the tailpipe temperature indicator. Indications of this instrument are balanced against turbine-rotor revolutions per minute, much in the same manner as manifold pressure is balanced against engine revolutions per minute in a conventional aircraft. The tailpipe temperature indicator consists of a series of open-type, chrome-alumel thermocouples, generally six in parallel. These units are arranged around the internal circumference of the tailpipe. With the enlargement of jet-powered aircraft, new types of temperature-recording instruments are needed. The heavy leads and critical low-resistance joints of thermocouple units are adaptable to relatively short-coupled aircraft installations. In the larger airplane designs, they are replaced by the resistance-bulb, ratio-type instrument. Research is focused on the development of a bulb which can withstand the elevated temperatures and corrosive atmosphere characteristic of the jet-powerplant tailpipe.

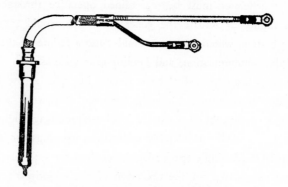

FIGURE 66. Jet-engine Thermocouple.

The conventional fuel-pressure gage is also used on the turbine-powered aircraft. In the jet-engine fuel-injection system, the fuel nozzle functions as a metering device and is extremely sensitive to variations in pressure. It would be expedient to calibrate the jet-engine fuel-pressure gage in terms of flow. The rapidly-changing nozzle characteristics tend to impose a definite obstacle to this arrangement.

Fuel flow meters, installed between the fuel pump and the combustion chamber must be of large capacity in order to meter the fuel properly. Both the rate and the pressure of fuel flow are considerably higher in the jet engine than in the piston engine. One type of jet-engine fuel pump, for example, delivers the equivalent of a barrel of fuel in 1 minute and 15 seconds under a pressure of 750 pounds per square inch. The fuel pressure in the piston engine rarely exceeds 25 pounds per square inch.

Flow meters indicate the rate at which fuel is supplied to the power-plant. These instruments give a rapid check on the functioning of the engine, since the rate at which fuel is being consumed will show up any deviation from normal operation. They also indicate the total fuel consumption, which, totalized over a given period of time, furnishes an accurate check on the fuel-quantity gage.

Standard oil-pressure gages are employed with aircraft turbine powerplants. The range of the instrument is dependent on the types of bearings and lubrication systems installed on the powerplants. Ball bearings will require comparatively low oil pressures, while sleeve bearings need high pressure. Turbine-engine pressure gages are, in general, fairly vibration-free. The high oil pressures required for starting in regions of very low ambient temperature may cause distor-

FIGURE 67. A British Turbojet Powerplant;
The Rolls Royce Nene Centrifugal-flow Unit.

tion and even destruction of the oil-pressure gages. Therefore, they are given high overpressure ratings.

A barometric fuel-control unit is provided for jet powerplant operation. The device maintains a constant power output in spite of variations in altitude. Since the jet powerplant can operate satisfactorily with a wide variety of fuels, and, primarily, hydrocarbons of low volatility, the fuel must be filtered prior to fueling the aircraft to protect the barometric fuel-control unit.

The compressor line is tapped for pressure required for the operation of the flight instruments. This is a departure from conventional practice, in which flight instruments are actuated by vacuum devices.

Recent models of jet-powered aircraft contain torque meters, synchroscopes, lubricating-oil dilution gages, recording tachometers, engine-operating time recorders, fuel-content gages, and flight-data recorders. Some means of thrust measurement during flight would, perhaps, offer the best index of jet-aircraft performance.

Chapter 7

CONSTRUCTION MATERIALS

HIGH-TEMPERATURE STRENGTH STEELS

For building jet-propelled aircraft powerplants, metals would be needed that combine the high strength to withstand rotational velocities of the order of 12,000 revolutions per minute and the elevated temperatures at which an internal-combustion turbine operates. The lack of such materials has retarded the aircraft-turbine development until very recent times. The tensile strength of most available steel alloys is reduced by 50 percent at temperatures of the order of 1,000° F. and, in addition, these metals "creep," or expand, at high temperatures and rotation speeds. This characteristic is most undesirable from the standpoint of the close tolerances between gas-turbine blading and its casing.

More recently, however, two outstanding steel alloys have been found suitable for the construction of turbine rotor blades: 16-25-6 alloy and Nimonic 80 alloy.

16-25-6 STEEL ALLOY

This is produced by the Timken Roller Bearing Co. and is used in practically all of the currently manufactured turbojet powerplants. It is an austenitic and nonmagnetic steel alloy, whose name indicates the percentage of chromium (16), nickel (25), and molybdenum (6) contained in it. Chromium is used because of its excellent corrosion and oxidation resistance; molybdenum contributes high-temperature strength. Nickel insures a purely austenitic structure and balances the chromium and molybdenum. The alloy contains minor amounts of other elements. Its low carbon content yields excellent welding and forging characteristics; nitrogen reduces "creep" at elevated temperatures; manganese improves forgeability; and silicon contributes to the scale resistance. The exact composition of 16-25-6 alloy is as follows.

Element	%
Carbon	0.12
Nitrogen	0.15
Silicon	1.00
Manganese	2.00
Molybdenum	6.00
Chromium	16.00
Nickel	25.00

Creep-strength tests, conducted at 1300 and 1400° F., indicated that the strength of 16-25-6 alloy is about four times as high as that of standard stainless steel.

The forging temperature of the improved 16-25-6 alloy is 2000° F. Turbine-rotor components for use with aircraft turbojet powerplants are produced in a 3,000-ton hydraulic forging press. The forging process consists of two steps: "hot working" and "cold working."

HOT WORKING AND COLD WORKING OF STEELS

During hot working, a definite billet or bloom is formed in a blocking die at a maximum temperature of 2000° F., which is then cold worked at 1200 to 1400° F. Drop hammers of 35,000 to 47,000 pounds are used for processing the blocked forging during the cold-working phase. Finally, the forging is tempered at 1200 to 1250° F. to relieve the extremely high stresses developed during the cold working.

The tensile-strength properties of 16-25-6 alloy are as follows:

Temperature	Yield Strength	Ultimate Strength	Elongation	Reduction of Area
°F.	psi	psi	%	%
Room	90,000 - 115,000	125,000-150,000	10-20	10-30
1500		55,000-65,000	15-30	15-40

NIMONIC 80 AND NIMONIC 90 STEEL ALLOYS

Nimonic 80 is a British product. It contains about 80 percent nickel, with chromium and titanium as the other chief ingredients. It is similar, in some respects, to the American alloy called Nichrome. Nimonic 80 is widely used for the manufacture of turbine-rotor blades. Nimonic 75 is a similar alloy, which is used for the fabrication of combustion-chamber linings, called "flame tubes" in England. In some of the British-designed jet powerplants, precision-cast vitallium nozzle blades are employed in preference to forged members. Very heavy equipment is required for the forging of structural members of vitallium alloys. The die life is short, yielding 1,500 to 2,000 turbine blades. For this reason, vitallium is not favored by aircraft metallurgists.

A newer, high-performance product, Nimonic 90, has a load-carrying capacity approximately 10 percent higher than Nimonic 80 at 750° C. (1400° F.). Nimonic 90 retains its physical properties up to a temperature of 870° C. (1600° F.).

INCONEL STEEL ALLOYS

Two high-nickel-content domestic alloys, suitable for jet-aircraft powerplants, are Inconel and Inconel X. Inconel is utilized primarily where high oxidation resistance is required and a moderate hot strength is sufficient, e.g., jet-burner liners, exhaust systems, and heater combustion chambers.

Inconel X, an age-hardenable alloy, offers high hot strength up to a temperature of 1500° F. Its oxidation resistance is also high. It is suitable for making turbine wheels and turbine blades, as well as engine structural members which are subjected to sustained high temperatures.

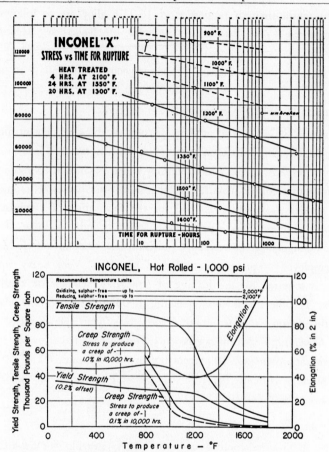

FIGURE 68. The Properties of Inconel Alloy.

TITANIUM

Titanium is comparatively a newcomer to the turbine-powerplant field. The jet-engine designer is primarily interested in its heat resistance. Pure titanium melts at 3272° F. Its corrosion resistance is comparable with that of 18-8 stainless steel and it is available in large quantities. Titanium has a favorable proportional limit of the order of 59,000 pounds per square inch annealed, and 84,000 pounds per square inch cold worked. As an aircraft structural metal, titanium is alloyed with 5 percent chromium and 3 percent aluminum. Titanium alloys cannot be used at temperatures higher than 1000° F.

It should be noted that a high melting point alone does not qualify a metal for high-performance aircraft application. Resistance to oxidation is also a vital factor. Some of the metals which have high melting points, but lack oxidation resistance are as follows:

Metal	*Melting Point* (°F.)
Thorium	3350
Zirconium	3450
Boron	4150
Molybdenum	4750
Tantalum	5100
Tungsten	6100

The previously mentioned titanium alloy is as strong as high-strength steel, but weighs only half as much. Its ready availability is of strategic importance. Additional research may yield a titanium alloy which is suitable for the fabrication of turbine-blade elements, tail-pipe shrouds, and fire walls. Nozzle blades, fabricated of stainless steel and stabilized with titanium and columbium, have proved very satisfactory in sustained service.

Commercially pure titanium can be readily welded, using either the Heliarc or resistance-welding processes. Care, however, must be taken to prevent contamination through absorption of gases. Brittleness occurs as a direct result of this.

Welding of alloyed titanium is still more difficult because of gas contamination. The main problem involves quench-hardening of the metal while cooling from welding temperatures. Other methods of joining titanium, notably flash butt welding and silver-alloy brazing, have also had difficulties, but some fairly suitable solutions have been found for the first method.

Machining and grinding of titanium alloys present difficulties because of the presence of abrasive particles of titanium carbide. However, new methods of melting have resulted in maintaining the carbon content at a minimum.*

Forging of titanium alloys, as in the case of jet-compressor disks, appears very promising.

CERAMICS

Fortunately, oxidation at elevated temperatures can be retarded by means of ceramic coatings. Steel alloys of adequate high-temperature (around 1500° F.) or hot-strength properties are available. However, if the operating temperatures of jet powerplants will be materially increased to achieve higher thermodynamic efficiencies, there will be such specifications for the high-temperature properties of metals which cannot be met with the metals now on the market. Ceramics may replace metals as primary structural materials in aircraft-powerplant design and production. As a matter of fact, they are being utilized for this purpose because of their excellent heat resistance. It has been suggested to protect low-melting alloys from high-velocity combustion gases at 5000° F. and possibly above by ceramic coatings. Ceramics of high mechanical and dielectric strength at temperatures up to 2000° F. are available for application in aircraft gas turbines. They contain aluminum, beryllium, thorium, and zirconium oxides, with minor additions of other metallic oxides.

The porcelain ceramics usually contain feldspar. This forms a flux with clay and silica which fills the interstices.

Static tests of 2,000 hours, conducted at 1800° F., with stresses ranging from 9,000 to 14,000 pounds per square inch within the ceramic test specimen, indicated an elongation of 0.23 percent. At temperatures above 1900° F., the elongation is much greater. Tests conducted at 1500 to 2000° F. showed the creep characteristics to be satisfactory.

Ceramic coatings have two basic functions. First, they seal the metal surface against corrosive action. Second, they provide thermal in-

---

* Melting titanium alloys by induction heating in a graphite crucible.

sulation. For employment as jet-engine coatings, only the enamel-type ceramics have proved suitable.

THERMAL SHOCK

Ceramic coatings are susceptible to thermal shock created by rapidly-moving flame fronts coming into sudden contact with cold turbine blades. This usually occurs at take-off, but it may result from failure of the air supply at any time. This disadvantage is partly eliminated in improved aircraft-turbojet designs by introducing fuel only to the two combustion chambers equipped with electric starting plugs. This arrangement differs from the original system in which the fuel was introduced simultaneously into all the combustion chambers of a turbojet powerplant. In the older models, when the starting plugs in the two combustion chambers are energized, flames spread circumferentially through interconnecting tubes to the remaining combustion chambers. The excess fuel vapors thus ignite violently, with resultant thermal shock to cold internal parts. This starting method is called the "hot start." In the newer system, the heat travels slowly from the two combustion chambers containing the energized starting plugs to the other combustion chambers. Following this initial increase in temperature, fuel is introduced into the remaining combustion chambers. Smooth, flameless starting at approximately 1350° F. is provided in this manner. Another means for the prevention of hot starts is the newly developed variable-area fuel nozzle. This device provides a fine, fully atomized spray to replace the large droplets of fuel previously introduced into the combustion unit and thus eliminates explosion and sudden rise of temperature.

A standard test for resistance to thermal shock consists in heating ceramic test specimens to a temperature of 1875° F., then plunging into cold water for repeated trials. The test is terminated by observing and reporting the condition of the test specimens.

CERAMIC COATINGS

A typical aircraft ceramic that has continuous strength between 1600 and 2000° F. is composed of 80 percent titanium carbide and 20 percent cobalt. An improved material containing 90 percent titanium carbide and 10 percent molybdenum has retained its physical properties up to 2400° F. Titanium carbide has also the best resistance to thermal shock of all the available ceramics. Hot-pressed ceramics have been found suitable for aircraft-powerplant application after adequate sintering or heat treatment. The hot-pressed ceramics usually contain magnesium oxide, zirconium carbide, boron carbide, silicon, and zirconium oxide.

One aircraft ceramic coating consists of a base coat of low-expansion frit with 20 percent zirconium oxide. Over this is a cover coat containing 95 percent zirconia. The top-seal coat consists of a thin layer of the base-coat material.

Ceramic coatings are applied in the form of water suspensions, called "slips," by spraying or dipping. After drying, the coated parts are fired at a temperature as high as 2150° F. in an oxygen-free atmosphere.

PRODUCTION PATTERN FOR CERAMIC COATINGS

Ceramic coatings are about 0.001 inch thick. They must necessarily have the same coefficient of expansion as that of the base metal. In the case of low-carbon steels, it is very desirable for the ceramic coating to fuse early in the heating cycle in order to seal off oxygen and thus prevent excessive oxidation of the base metal. Fusion on ceramics contemplated for high-strength alloys is delayed until sufficient metal oxide is formed to insure adequate adhesion.

The step-by-step production pattern for the ceramic coating of metal jet-engine components is as follows:

    (a) scaling—cleaning of the base metal part at 1800° F.

    (b) pickling—successive passage of the base metal part through an acid bath, a high-pressure water spray, a drying period, and a final acid bath.

(c) burning-off—a surface exposure to a temperature of 1875° F. to burn the acid residue off the base metal part.

(d) sandblasting—this is done to prepare the metal surface for coating.

(e) application of coating—this may be accomplished either by dipping or spraying. Frequently, both techniques are employed and then the dipping is done first.

(f) firing of the coating—this is done in a furnace at 1875° F.

(g) interim and final inspections—these include checking of coating composition and thermal-shock determinations.

Ceramics can be stripped and reprocessing accomplished, if necessary. This may be done only once, however. Further recycling appears to harm the base metal.

Ceramic coatings are used primarily to conserve critical construction materials, such as columbium, nickel, tungsten, cobalt, and molybdenum.

METAL-CERAMIC COMBINATIONS

Various metal-ceramic combinations have proved to be even more heat resistant than the pure ceramic materials. These products are very suitable for aircraft use, since the pure ceramic members must be rimmed with metal to resist centrifugally applied loads. Ceremal is the trade name covering one of these combinations. It is obtained by fusing ceramics and metal alloys. Another trade-name product, Mercast, is a combination of mercury and a ceramic material.

The most promising aircraft-engine ceramic so far developed is molybdenum disilicide, an intermetallic chemical combination produced by powder metallurgy. The density of this product is low and its resistance to heat and oxidation is high. The low density of molybdenum disilicide is a great advantage as it will limit the centrifugal forces induced in turbine blades.

Some of the newer ceramics, although inferior to Ceremal below 2500° F., have proved very effective at 3000 to 3500° F. A combination of boron carbide and iron is in this group. The strength of this and other similar ceramic combinations is about one-third of that of molybdenum disilicide.

It has been suggested to manufacture turbine blades for aircraft powerplants entirely from ceramics. Ceramics would be suitable for stator blades. However, their brittleness and the fact that they offer much more resistance to compression than to tension would drastically limit their use as rotor blades. Some oxide ceramics have ten times higher compressive strength than tensile strength. An exceptional case would be a design in which the rotor blades would be subjected to compressive loads only, or where the blades could be prestressed. Then again, the lack of ductility, characteristic of these materials, may prevent their use.

If it were possible to replace metal turbine blades with ceramic blades, this would result in reduced weight and cost. In any event, the suitability of ceramics for use as structural members in aircraft turbine powerplants will represent some sort of compromise between the factors of strength and resistance to elevated temperatures and thermal shock.

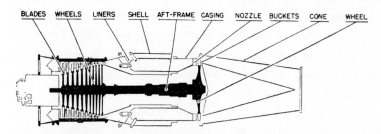

FIGURE 69. Application of Substitute, Nonstrategic Materials to a Conventional Turbojet Powerplant.

NON-STRATEGIC MATERIALS

In case of a national emergency, the manufacture of aircraft-turbine powerplants from nonstrategic materials would help conserve critical construction materials. Some loss of engine life and performance may be anticipated under these conditions. It is felt, however, that the net over-all gain would justify this shortcoming. Figure 69 illustrates a typical aircraft turbojet powerplant. Table II applies to the high-performance, strategic materials for its construction. Table I applies to the substitute, noncritical construction materials.

TABLE I			TABLE II		
Part	Material	Approx. Weight, Pounds	Part	Material	Approx. Weight, Pounds
Exhaust Cone	N-155	200	Exhaust Cone	Type 316	200
Turbine Wheel	Timken	150	Turbine Wheel	Timken	125
Turbine Buckets	Vitallium	100	Turbine Buckets	Nimonic 80	100
Turbine Nozzle Blades	X-40	100	Turbine Nozzle Blades	N-155	100
Turbine Casing	19-9DL	50	Turbine Casing	Low Alloy Steel	50
Combustion Liner	N-155	50	Combustion Liner	Type 316	50
Combustion Shell	19-9DL	50	Shell	Low Alloy Steel	50
Main Frame	19-9DL	250	Main Frame	Low Alloy Steel	250
Compressor Wheels	Type 403	200	Compressor Wheels	Low Alloy Steel	200
Compressor Blades	Type 410	100	Compressor Blades	Low Alloy Steel	100

APPENDIX

Data of evolution of, and presently available, aircraft turbojet and turboprop powerplants and military and transport jet-propelled airplanes.

POWERPLANTS

GENERAL ELECTRIC COMPANY, SCHENECTADY, NEW YORK; LOCKLAND, OHIO

I-40—Centrifugal-flow Turbojet Powerplant. Develops 4,000 pounds thrust. Weighs 1,820 pounds. The weight/output ratio indicates an approximate weight of 1 pound per 2½ equivalent horsepower. This powerplant was employed to power the Lockheed Aircraft Corporation's "F-80" and the Bell Aircraft Corporation's "XF-83." An earlier version, the "I-16," powered the Bell Aircraft Corporation's pioneer jet-propelled airplane, the "P-59." Designated as the J-33, the powerplant is being manufactured by the Allison Division of General Motors Corporation, at Indianapolis. An improved version, equipped with a water-injection device, is rated at 4,500 pounds static sea-level thrust. Model "400," a further modification of the basic design, is rated at 4,600 pounds thrust dry and 5,500 pounds thrust when equipped with alcohol-water injection. It is generally assumed that a 20 to 25 percent increase in basic thrust output can be attained with water injection.

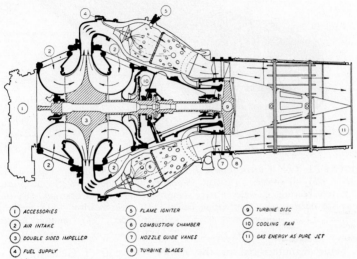

(1) ACCESSORIES	(5) FLAME IGNITER	(9) TURBINE DISC
(2) AIR INTAKE	(6) COMBUSTION CHAMBER	(10) COOLING FAN
(3) DOUBLE SIDED IMPELLER	(7) NOZZLE GUIDE VANES	(11) GAS ENERGY AS PURE JET
(4) FUEL SUPPLY	(8) TURBINE BLADES	

FIGURE 70. The Pratt and Whitney J-48 Turbojet Powerplant.

TG-100—Axial-flow Turbojet Powerplant. Develops 400 pounds thrust plus 1,900 horsepower. This powerplant, which actuates a conventional aircraft propeller on the forward end of its central power shaft, in addition to its rearwardly-directed jet discharge, was employed to power the Consolidated Vultee Corporation's "XF-81" pioneer fighter airplane, together with an I-40 pure-jet unit. It is also called the "T-31." It replaced the conventional reciprocating engine in the newer, modified version of the Ryan "Fireball" naval fighter aircraft described elsewhere in this text.

TG-180—Axial-flow Turbojet Powerplant. Develops 4,000 pounds thrust. Weighs 2,250 pounds. This turbojet unit is employed to power the Republic Aviation Company's F-84 "Thunderjet" fighter airplane. It was also used to power the Douglas Aircraft Company's pioneer "XB-43" bombardment airplane. Designated the J-35, this powerplant

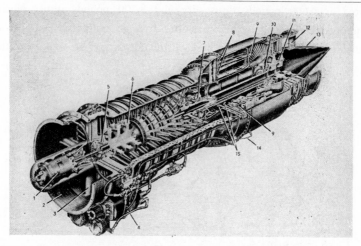

FIGURE 71. *The Westinghouse J-34 Turbojet Powerplant:* (1) starter motor; (2) oil cooler; (3) strut (accessory drive housing); (4) accessories; (5) front bearing; (6) eleven-stage compressor; (7) center bearings; (8) fuel-injection nozzles; (9) combustion basket; (10) rear bearing; (11) two-stage turbine; (12) support strut; (13) exhaust cone; (14) ignition harness; (15) oil lines.

is being manufactured by the Allison Division of General Motors Corporation, at Indianapolis, Indiana. When equipped with water-injection and thrust-augmentation devices, the thrust output is practically doubled. The J-35 axial-flow powerplant powers a number of tactical jet aircraft in current use.

TG-190—Axial-flow Turbojet Powerplant. Designated the "J-47," this powerplant is being manufactured by the General Electric Company, Aircraft Gas Turbine Division, West Lynn, Massachusetts. Weighs 2,500 pounds. It develops 5,200 pounds thrust without augmentation. It powers the Boeing Airplane Company's "B-47," bomber, and the Republic Aviation Company's "F-91" interceptor fighter.

WESTINGHOUSE ELECTRIC AND MANUFACTURING COMPANY, SOUTH PHILADELPHIA, PENNSYLVANIA

19-B—Axial-flow Turbojet Powerplant. Develops 1,365 pounds thrust. Weighs 824 pounds. This turbojet is employed to power the

FIGURE 72. The Westinghouse Y-ducted J-40-WE-6 Turbojet Powerplant.

McDonnell Navy "Phantom" fighter airplane. It also powered the Northrop-USAF "XF-79" fighter airplane, the "Flying Ram." This powerplant was followed by a more recent development, the "24-C" axial-flow turbojet powerplant (the symbol "24" representing the engine diameter in inches). The 24-C with an afterburner can develop 3,200 pounds static sea-level thrust. The thrust augmentation device, in this case, is considered responsible for an approximate 30 percent

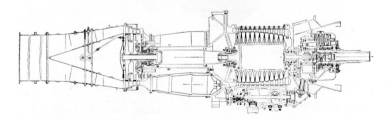

FIGURE 73. Profile View of the Armstrong-Siddeley "Mamba" Turbopropjet Powerplant.

increase in basic thrust output. Weighs 1,300 pounds. Powered the Curtiss "XF-87," the Douglas "Skyrocket," the McDonnell parasite fighter, the "XF-85," the "XF-88" interceptor, and the Lockheed "F-90" interceptor. An even newer and larger model has been designated the "J-34." Westinghouse also manufactures a small turbojet powerplant, the "9.5-A" of 275 pounds rated thrust, for the purpose of powering guided missiles.

Pratt and Whitney Aircraft Division, United Aircraft Corporation, East Hartford, Connecticut

JT-6B—Centrifugal-flow turbojet Powerplant. This is a redesign of the Rolls-Royce "Nene" powerplant. It develops 5,000 pounds thrust. Weighs 1,723 pounds. It powers the Grumman Aircraft Engineering Corporation's "F9F" naval shipboard fighter. It is also designated the "J-42."

JT-7—Centrifugal-flow Turbojet Powerplant. It is a redesign of the Roll-Royce "Tay" powerplant. It develops 6,250 pounds thrust alone and 8,000 pounds with an afterburner. It powers North American Aviation Incorporated's "F-93" fighter aircraft as the "J-48."

FIGURE 74. The British Armstrong-Siddeley "Double Mamba" Turbopropjet Powerplant.

PT-2—Turboprop Powerplant. Designated also the "T-34." It develops 5,700 shaft horsepower within a single unit. It weighs 2,550 pounds. It was developed jointly with the Navy, with a view to its powering several existing types of naval tactical aircraft.

ALLISON DIVISION, GENERAL MOTORS CORPORATION,
INDIANAPOLIS, INDIANA

501—Turboprop Powerplant. It is designated also as the "T-38."
It develops 2,750 shaft horsepower. It weighs 1,225 pounds, complete
with shafting and reduction gear.

500—Turboprop Powerplant. It is designated also the "T-40." This
is a combination of two T-38 powerplants, driving coaxial propellers
through a reduction gear. It develops 5,500 shaft horsepower. It
weighs 2,500 pounds, complete with shafting and reduction gear. It
powers the Douglas Aircraft Company's "A2D," and Convair's "P5Y"
long-range flying boat, the second with the aid of extension shafts. Also
in the advanced research and testing stages are the Allison "T-56"
turboprop powerplant developing 3,750 eshp. The "T-54" comprises
a double T-56 powerplant, coupled to a single set of propellers and developing 7,500 eshp.

FIGURE 75. The Allison "T-40" Turboprop Powerplant with Shaft Extension
Installation for the Navy "P5Y-1" Flying Boat.

TURBODYNE CORPORATION, NORTHROP AIRCRAFT,
INCORPORATED, HAWTHORNE, CALIFORNIA

Turbodyne-2—Turboprop Powerplant. It is designated also the
"T-37." It develops 10,000 shaft horsepower. It was recently purchased
by General Electric Company for further research and development.

MENASCO MANUFACTURING COMPANY, LOS ANGELES, CALIFORNIA

XJ-37—Turbojet Powerplant with an Axial-flow Compressor and
a Multistage Turbine. It is rated at 5,000 pounds static sea-level thrust.
The combined effects of thrust augmentation devices, including a

ducted fan and an afterburner, permit approximately 50 percent increase in thrust output, or 7,500 pounds total.

WRIGHT AERONAUTICAL CORPORATION, WOOD-RIDGE, NEW JERSEY

XT-35—Turboprop Powerplant. It has thirty-six radially disposed burners. A conventional aircraft propeller is rotated through a 10 to 1 reduction gearing. It develops 5,500 shaft horsepower. It was contemplated for installation in the Boeing Airplane Company's projected "XB-55" medium bombardment airplane. A Wright-designed turboprop adaptation of the British Armstrong-Siddeley "Sapphire" turbojet powerplant is now undergoing service tests.

FAIRCHILD ENGINE AND AIRPLANE CORPORATION, FARMINGDALE, L.I., N.Y.

XJ-44—Expendable Turbojet Powerplant. This unit is probably intended to power guided missiles. Develops 1,000 pounds thrust. Weighs 325 pounds, complete with accessories. Its dimensions are: diameter—22 inches; length—6 feet.

FIGURE 76. The Allison J-35-23 Turbojet Powerplant.

Other prominent American Manufacturers entering the field of aircraft turbojet and turboprop powerplant production include: Chrysler Motors, Allis-Chalmers, Ranger, DeLaval, Frederick Flader, and John Hawkins' Associates.

The race among nations for greater thrust output continues. Last-minute developments disclose a new Russian-built turbojet powerplant, the "Shvetsov," for which 12,300 pounds thrust, with afterburner, is claimed. The British Rolls-Royce "AJ-85," and "AJ-500," indicate 8,375 and 10,000 pounds thrust respectively, with afterburner. The English Bristol Company's "Olympus" jet also attains 10,000 pounds thrust. The Swedish Stal Svenska Turbinfabriks has pooled resources with Sweden's Svenska Flygmotor to produce a 10,000-pound-thrust turbojet powerplant.

However, not to be outdone, Pratt and Whitney has recently released the "J-57" turbojet, reported to have two separate compressor units and to develop 10,000 pounds thrust. Westinghouse now offers the "J-40" and the "J-46," turbojet powerplants, the second reportedly developing 12,500 pounds thrust with an afterburner. The Allison J-35-A-23, recently redesignated the J-71 by USAF, produces 9,000 pounds thrust. The J-73, redesignated General Electric J-47-21, gives a comparable power output.

Perhaps one of the strangest of recent powerplant developments is the British Napier "Nomad" composite diesel-turbine of 3,000 shaft horsepower output. The diesel component rotates one of two contra-

FIGURE 77. The Lockheed F-80 "Shooting Star."

rotating propellers, as well as an axial and a centrifugal compressor. The turbine portion rotates the other propeller. This powerplant is noted for its remarkably low fuel consumption.

FIGURE 78. The Lockheed F-80A-1 Airplane.

AIRPLANES

LOCKHEED AIRCRAFT CORPORATION, BURBANK, CALIFORNIA

F-80—Single-place Fighter Airplane. An all-metal, midwing monoplane of semimonocoque construction, with a tricycle landing gear. Wing span is 39 feet. Fuselage length is 34 feet, 6 inches. Height from the ground to the top of the vertical fin is 11 feet, 4 inches. Weight is 8,000 pounds empty, and approximately 14,000 pounds with full military load, including ammunition, photographic equipment, bombs, and fuel. All outer covering is flush riveted and treated with a special high-gloss wax polish to reduce surface drag. Attained performance includes over 550 miles per hour true air speed and a 45,000 feet ceiling. Special features are a hydraulic aileron boost, electrically operated wing flaps, a pressurized cockpit, droppable wing-tip fuel tanks, and a miniature refrigeration unit for cooling the pressurized cockpit air. This airplane has exceptionally clean aerodynamic lines which are reflected in excellent performance in compressibility regions.

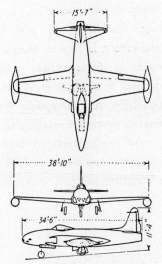

FIGURE 79. Three Views of the Lockheed F-80 Airplane.

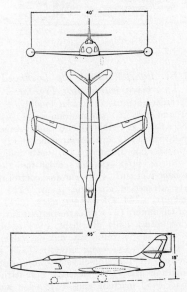

FIGURE 80. Three Views of the Lockheed F-90 Penetration Fighter.

F-90—Single-place Penetration Fighter Airplane. It is designed for fighting far behind enemy lines, where it will strike at airfields, supply depots, and lines of communication. Essential requirements are high speed and long range. Wing span is 40 feet. Over-all length, including pitot tube and mount, is 56 feet. Height from the ground to the top of the vertical fin is 16 feet. Gross weight approximates 13 tons. Wings are swept back at an angle of 35° and are claimed to be of the thinnest construction yet attempted. The first swept-wing design which had external, droppable wingtip fuel tanks, made possible by the application of newly developed, high-strength aluminum alloys. Vertical and horizontal fins are swept back at an angle of 45°. It is powered by two Westinghouse J-34, multistage-compressor, axial-

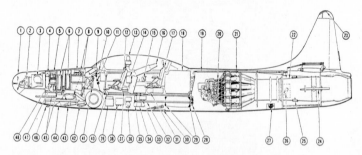

FIGURE 81. *Equipment of the Lockheed F-94 Two-place Interceptor Fighter:*

(1) plastic nose; (2) radar antenna; (3) radar modulator; (4) oxygen bottle; (5) radar range servo gear box; (6) ammunition boxes (4); (7) C-1 position light flasher; (8) AN/ARC-3 and AN/ARN-6 radio receivers; (9) gun-sight; (10) pilot's radar indicator; (11) instrument panel; (12) pilot's seat; (13) AN/ARN-6 radio compass loop antenna; (14) radar indicator power supply; (15) radar manual control; (16) operator's radar indicator; (17) radar operator's seat; (18) fuselage fuel tank; (19) elevator control rod; (20) J33-A-33 engine; (21) fuselage aft-section attaching point; (22) afterburner; (23) AN/ARC-3 radio antenna; (24) afterburner track; (25) afterburner eyelid actuator; (26) elevator tab motor; (27) gyrosyn compass flux valve; (28) aileron booster unit; (29) wing beams; (30) dive flaps; (31) turbine and cooler unit; (32) aileron torque tube; (33) cabin air mixing valve; (34) interphone amplifier; (35) D-2 inverter; (36) radar inverter; (37) radar vertical gyro; (38) radar; (39) batteries; (40) aileron-elevator control assembly (41) rudder pedals; (42) nose alighting gear; (43) fuselage nose-section attaching point; (44) case ejection door; (45) machine guns (4); (46) air-speed pitot; (47) gun-sight computer; (48) gun-sight amplifier servo.

flow turbojet powerplants, providing a total of 6,000 pounds thrust. Range is 2,000 miles when operations are conducted above 40,000 feet. When equipped with afterburners, the F-90 airplane can attain speeds in the supersonic range.

F-94—Two-place Interceptor Fighter Airplane. An ultimate evolution of the "T-33" jet trainer version of the F-80 airplane; an all-weather design. Accommodates a radar operator and approximately 3,000 pounds of equipment in addition to the pilot. Gross weight is 15,000 pounds. The Allison "400-D9" powerplant of 6,000 pounds thrust propels the F-94 at over 600 miles per hour speeds. A Solar afterburner is provided for short bursts of extra power.

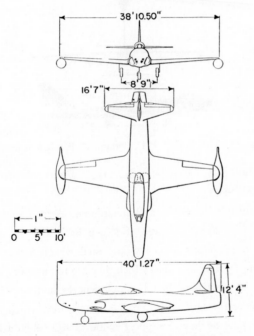

FIGURE 82. The Lockheed F-94 Airplane.

F-97—A Variation of the F-94 Airplane, with Very Thin, Straight Wing Members. It is powered by a Pratt and Whitney J-48 turbojet powerplant. Fitted with an afterburner, this unit develops 8,000 pounds thrust. Performance in the region of Mach 1 is anticipated with this design. USAF has redesignated the F-97 as the F-94C.

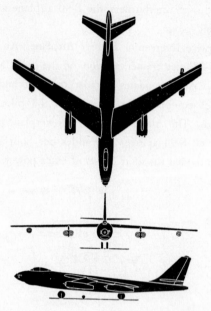

FIGURE 83. The Boeing B-47 "Stratojet" Bombardment Airplane.

BOEING AIRPLANE COMPANY, SEATTLE, WASHINGTON AND WICHITA, KANSAS

B-47—Multiple Jet-engined Bombardment Airplane. A high-wing monoplane with a high degree of sweep back and a "bicycle" type landing gear. Two sets of heavy-duty dual wheels are mounted fore and aft along the fuselage, into which they are retractable. The forward wheel set is steerable. Small, single-wheel landing-gear legs are mounted beneath each inboard engine nacelle, into which they retract, in order to provide lateral support while at rest and during taxiing, take-off, and landing. The bicycle arrangement is necessary because of the thin wing construction which cannot serve as housing for retractable landing gear members. Wing span is 116 feet. Over-all length is 108 feet. Gross weight is 124,000 pounds. It is powered by six General Electric-Allison J-35 axial-flow turbojet powerplants, providing a total of 24,000 pounds rated thrust. Four powerplant units are suspended in pairs on either side of the fuselage. The remaining two powerplants are mounted singly near each wing tip. In this manner, the wing structure supports the weight of the outboard powerplants and prevents the bending of the attaching fittings between the fuselage and the thin wing spar members. For take-off or acceleration during flight, auxiliary power is provided by two batteries of nine 1,000-pound "Jato" rocket units. The rocket motors are mounted on either side of the fuselage, aft of the wing root. When activated, the Jato units provide 18,000 pounds additional thrust for 2.8 seconds. Performance figures include a maximum speed of 630 miles per hour at 30,000 feet and 720 miles per hour in a dive. Mach 0.95 can be attained before serious drag complications are encountered. The wing

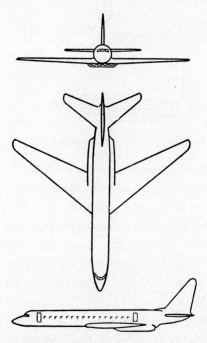

FIGURE 84. The Lockheed "L-193" Turbojet-powered Transport Airplane.

panels, vertical fin, and horizontal stabilizer are designed with a 45°
sweep back in order to minimize the adverse effects of compressibility.

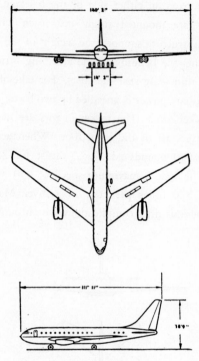

FIGURE 85. The Boeing "473" Turbojet-powered Transport Airplane.

XB-52—An Eight-engined Version of the B-47. The original proto-
type was contemplated to be powered by eight turboprop powerplants
coupled to four contrarotating propellers. Due to a shift in USAF
policy, the newest design incorporates eight Pratt and Whitney "J-57"
axial-flow turbojet powerplants. Anticipated performance of the
XB-52 includes a top speed over 500 miles per hour at an operational
altitude above 45,000 feet. No further dimensional or performance
data are available.

XB-56—A Four-jet-engined Version of the B-47. Four Allison
"J-35-AL3" turbojet powerplants, developing 9,700 pounds thrust each,

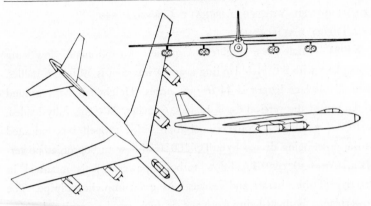

FIGURE 86. The Boeing XB-52 "Stratofortress" Bombardment Airplane.

were substituted for the six General Electric J-47 turbojets of the original design. USAF subsequently redesignated the XB-56 as the B-47C. A last-minute move has indicated that the entire project will now be abandoned.

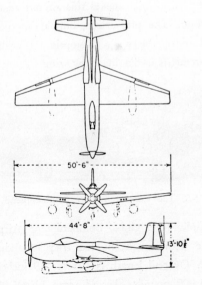

FIGURE 87. The F-81 Consolidated Vultee Fighter.

CONSOLIDATED VULTEE AIRCRAFT CORPORATION,
SAN DIEGO, CALIFORNIA

XF-81—Single-place Fighter Airplane. An all-metal, low-wing monoplane with a tricycle landing gear. Wing span is 50 feet, 6 inches. Over-all fuselage length is 44 feet, 8 inches. Height from the ground to the top of the vertical fin is 13 feet, 6 inches. Weight, fully loaded, is 19,500 pounds. A conventional four-bladed propeller is mounted in the nose, being driven by a TG-100 axial-flow turbopropjet powerplant. An I-40 centrifugal-flow turbojet powerplant is mounted in the rear of the aircraft and exhausts its gases into the tailpipe. The powerplants, both utilizing kerosene as fuel, can be employed either singly or in unison. Two large airscoops, located in the midsection of the fuselage, provide air for the rear-mounted, pure-jet powerplant. Air for the forward turbopropjet powerplant is introduced at the base of the propeller spinner member. Performance characteristics credit the craft with a speed of 550 miles per hour and a ceiling of 40,000 feet. It can perform efficiently from sea-level to maximum ceiling due to its dual powerplants which makes this aircraft adaptable as a long-range escort fighter. The pressurized, bubble-canopied cockpit is located well forward of the wing for optimum visibility. A special feature of the aircraft is its laminar-flow wing.

FIGURE 88. The Convair XB-46 Bombardment Airplane.

XB-46—Multiple Jet-engined Bombardment Airplane. A high-wing monoplane with a conventional tricycle landing gear. Wing span is 113 feet. Over-all length is 105 feet, 9 inches. Gross weight approximates 91,000 pounds. According to USAF classification, this aircraft falls into the medium bombardment weight category. It is powered by four General Electric-Allison J-35 axial-flow turbojet powerplants, providing a total of 16,000 pounds rated thrust. The powerplants are arranged in pairs in twin nacelles located on either side of the fuselage. The XB-46 is manned by a crew of three. An unusual feature of this airplane is the pneumatic system for the actuation of the landing gear with which it is provided. The maximum speed approximates 500 miles per hour.

FIGURE 89. The Convair F-92 (Redesignated F-102) Fighter Airplane.

F-92—Single-place Fighter Airplane. Designated as Model 7002 by the manufacturer. Wing span is 31 feet. Over-all length is 41 feet. Height of the vertical fin from the ground is 18 feet. It is powered by the Allison J-33 turbojet powerplant which is rated up to 5,200 pounds thrust, with the use of water injection. Supplementary rocket power is also provided. Operating characteristics include speeds in the high subsonic range at altitudes above 40,000 feet. The wing of the F-92 airplane is in the form of an equilateral triangle and is designated as a "delta wing." The leading edge has a 60° sweep back, while that of the conventional jet-powered aircraft is only about 35°. So-called "elevons" in the trailing edge function as elevators and ailerons, thus compensating for the absence of a conventional tail section. The planform of the delta wing combines a high wing sweepback and a low aspect ratio, both of which are favorable for supersonic flight. Since dynamic pressures at supersonic speed have a high value, lift coefficients need not be large. The primary advantage of the delta wing is its low drag. This aircraft has been redesignated as the F-102 by the USAF.

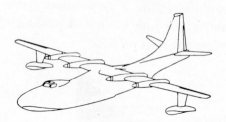

FIGURE 90. The Navy Convair "XP5Y-1" Turboprop-powered Patrol Flying Boat.

P5Y-1—Turboprop Naval Flying Boat. Wing span is 146 feet. Over-all length is 130 feet. Hull beam is 10 feet. Has a high hull-length to beam ratio. Gross weight approximates 60 tons. It is powered by four double-unit Allison T-40 turboprop powerplants, developing 5,500 shaft horsepower each and rotating eight-bladed "Aeromatic" propellers. Later models have six-bladed, 180-inch "Aeroproducts" propellers. Maximum speed is of the order of 400 miles per hour. Range is more than 3,500 miles. The P5Y-1 holds the world's endurance record of 8 hours, 6 minutes for this type of aircraft. A cargo version, the R3Y-1, is similar in all of the described respects, except that of hull accommodations.

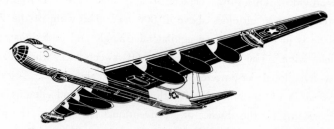

FIGURE 91. The Convair "B-36D" Bombardment Airplane.

B-36D—Six-engined (piston) Heavy Bombardment Airplane. It is additionally equipped with four General Electric J-47 turbojet power-plants, mounted in pairs in pods under each wing. The jet engines furnish additional performance during emergency combat maneuvers and over-the-target runs. The total power output of the six Pratt and Whitney "Wasp Major" engines (3,800 horsepower each) plus the thrust developed by the turbojet powerplants aggregates a maximum figure of about 44,000 horsepower. By utilizing this power, the airplane can attain over 435 miles per hour maximum speed, and a service ceiling of 45,000 feet. Wing span is 230 feet. Over-all length is 162 feet. Height from the ground to the top of the vertical stabilizer is 46 feet, 9 inches.

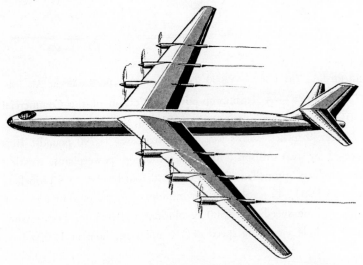

FIGURE 92. Originally planned Turboprop-powered Version of the Convair B-36F.

XB-60—Swept-wing, Jet-powered Configuration of the B-36. This was originally designed as a turboprop-powered configuration, incorporating tractor propellers. The finally accepted model is powered by eight Pratt and Whitney J-57 axial-flow turbojet powerplants. These are mounted in pairs in pods under each wing panel. Anticipated performance of the turbojet-powered XB-60 is a maximum speed of 550 miles per hour at a tactical altitude of 55,000 feet.

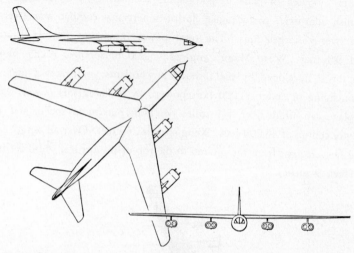

FIGURE 93. The Convair YB-60 Turbojet-powered Bombardment Airplane.

"Turboliner"—A Turboprop-powered Version of the Commercial "240" "Convair Liner." Wing span is 91 feet, 9 inches. Over-all length is 74 feet, 8 inches. Gross weight approximates 41,790 pounds. It is powered by two Allison "501-A4" turboprop powerplants, rotating "Aeroproducts" propellers. The 13½-foot, four-bladed, steel propellers are rotated at 1,146 revolutions per minute, or in the ratio of 12.5 to 1 to the turbine speed of 14,300 revolutions per minute. Performance figures include a cruising speed of 310 miles per hour at 16,000 feet.

FIGURE 94. The Curtiss XF-87 Fighter Airplane.

The Turboliner is used as a civil-cargo airplane test bed for turboprop powerplants. Comparative data for the piston-engined and turbine-engined aircraft are as follows:

	Convair Liner	*Turboliner*
Gross weight	41,790	41,790
Maximum fuel capacity	1,000 gal.	1,500 gal.
Maximum range	920 stat. mi.	1,200-1,600 stat. mi. (depending on fuel used)
Average cruising air speed (at 16,000 ft., 75% rated power, weight 39,000 to 42,000 lbs.)	272 m.p.h.	310 m.p.h
Maximum level-flight speed	347 m.p.h.	350 m.p.h
Powerplants	P&W R-2800	Allison 501
Maximum take-off horsepower	4,800	5,500
Service ceiling	24,300 ft.	32,500 ft.
Sea-level rate of climb	1,500 ft./min.	1,940 ft./min.

CURTISS-WRIGHT AIRCRAFT CORPORATION, COLUMBUS, OHIO

XF-87—Two-place, Multiple-jet-engined Fighter Airplane. This is a mid-wing monoplane with a conventional tricycle landing gear. Wing span is 65 feet. Over-all length is 60 feet. Gross weight approximates 30,000 pounds. It is powered by four Westinghouse 24-C axial-flow turbojet powerplants, developing a total of 12,000 pounds static thrust. The small (24-inch) diameter of this powerplant makes possible installation in pairs in twin nacelles located on either side of the fuselage. Variable-thrust "plugs" are fitted into the tailpipe, which —being controllable during flight—permit variations of thrust without adversely affecting either engine speed or operating efficiency. A certain amount of lift is contributed over the nacelle region. The XF-87 is an "all-weather" airplane, incorporating "hot wing" deicing equipment along the leading edge of the wing panels, vertical fin, and horizontal stabilizer units. Specially designed air-intake ducts, leading to the jet powerplants, prevent icing and moisture induction. Performance figures include a maximum speed of 620 miles per hour and a service ceiling of 40,000 feet. Rated speed at 20,000 feet is 585 miles per hour. Rate of climb is more than 6,000 feet per minute. Its range being 2,000 miles, it can be used as an escort for strategic bombardment aircraft. The wing panels are of the laminar-flow, airfoil type, tapered, and of cantilever design. Four small flap panels are mounted on either side of the powerplant nacelles. Slots are provided in the leading edges of the wings in order to attain stable air flow over the aileron region during high angle of attack conditions. The streamlined "bubble" cabin is pressurized for high-altitude operations. Both crew members are equipped with ejection seats for high-speed escape in emergency.

FIGURE 95. The Bell XF-83 Airplane.

BELL AIRCRAFT CORPORATION, BUFFALO, NEW YORK

XF-83—Single-place Fighter Airplane. Although similar in outline and general appearance to the pioneer jet-propelled Bell "P-59" airplane, this twin-engined aircraft is larger and capable of better performance. It is an all-metal, midwing monoplane of semimonocoque construction, with a tricycle landing gear. Wing span is 53 feet. Fuselage length is 44 feet, 10 inches. Height from the ground to the top of the vertical fin is 15 feet, 3 inches. Weight, fully loaded, is 27,000 pounds. The empennage group is upswept to permit the control surfaces to entirely clear the jet blasts of the twin outboard I-40 turbojet powerplants. Its speed is 550 miles per hour and its ceiling, 40,000 feet. The cockpit is fitted with a bubble canopy and located well forward of the wing to afford optimum visibility.

FIGURE 96. The Republic F-84 Airplane in Flight.

FIGURE 97. The Republic F-84 Airplane.

REPUBLIC AVIATION CORPORATION, FARMINGDALE, LONG ISLAND, NEW YORK

F-84—Single-place Fighter Airplane. An all-metal, low-midwing monoplane with a retractable tricycle landing gear. Wing span is 36 feet, 5 inches. Over-all length is 37 feet. Weight, fully loaded, is approximately 15,000 pounds. The outer covering of the aircraft is flush-riveted and highly polished to reduce the surface drag to a minimum. Flight-test performance indicates a speed of over 590 miles per hour, a service range of 1,000 miles, and a service ceiling of 40,000 feet. Its air scoop is located in the nose of the fuselage, in contrast to the conventional side arrangement. Special features include a high-speed, thin airfoil section; an electrically operated, jettisonable bubble canopy; a pilot ejection seat for emergency exits; an air-conditioned pressure cabin; and provision for mounting external wing-tip auxiliary fuel tanks. The rear section of the fuselage is readily removable, so that the J-35 turbojet powerplant can be completely replaced within 50 minutes.

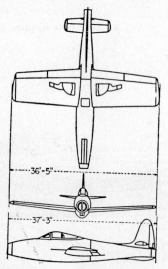

FIGURE 98. Three views of the Republic F-84 Airplane.

F-91—Single-place, Interceptor Fighter Airplane. Wing span is 30 feet. Over-all length is 45 feet. Height from the ground to the top of the vertical fin is 15 feet. It is powered by a General Electric J-47 turbojet powerplant plus four rocket motors. The F-91 is designed to operate at speeds approximating that of sound. A distinctive feature is an inverse taper of its main wing panels. The chord of the wing is greater at the tip than at the root, a drastic departure from conventional practice. The wings are claimed to be the thinnest yet constructed for a military aircraft. A similar claim has been made for the wings of the F-90 airplane which has been discussed previously. The landing gear of the F-91 aircraft is also unusual in that it has tandem main landing wheels located at the midspan of the wing panels. A later version is designated the F-103.

FIGURE 99. The Republic F-91 Fighter Airplane.

XF-96—A Swept-wing Version of the F-84 Airplane. It has been recently redesignated by the United States Air Force as F-84F. Wing span is 34 feet. Over-all length is 38 feet. Height from the ground to the top of the vertical fin is 14 feet. Maximum gross weight approximates 25,000 pounds. It is powered by an Allison J-35-25 turbojet powerplant. No afterburner is provided. Later models will be powered by Curtiss Wright-built Armstrong Siddeley "Sapphire" turbojet powerplants, developing 7,200 pounds rated thrust. This British-designed powerplant is now designated by the United States Air Force as the J-65.

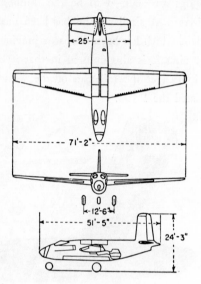

FIGURE 100. Three views of the Douglas XB-43 Airplane.

DOUGLAS AIRCRAFT COMPANY, SANTA MONICA, CALIFORNIA

XB-43—Twin Jet-engined Bombardment Airplane. This is a midwing monoplane, with a fold-back, retractable tricycle landing gear. Wing span is 71 feet, 2 inches. Over-all length is 51 feet, 6 inches. Its aerodynamically clean contour is the result of housing its twin TG-180 turbojet powerplants in the fuselage. This is a pronounced departure from the conventional practice of mounting twin-jet powerplants outboard on the wing panels. Performance characteristics include a speed over 500 miles per hour, an operational range of 1,400 miles, and a service ceiling of 38,000 feet. Complete cabin pressurization is provided for crew comfort.

XS-3—(Skystreak) (Project designation "D-558") This is a single-place, research aircraft, designed for transonic tests; a low-wing mono-

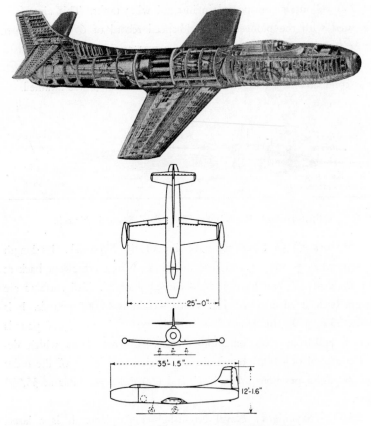

FIGURE 101. The Douglas XS-3 "Skystreak."

plane with a tricycle landing gear. Wing span is 25 feet. Over-all length is 35 feet, 1.5 inches. Height from the ground to the top of the vertical fin is 12 feet. Gross weight is 9,750 pounds. The fuselage nose section can be jettisoned and separates from the aircraft in emergency. The rear fuselage is a magnesium sheet section, supported by vertical formers. It is designed for a load factor of 18. Provision is made for 500 pounds of test instruments to be installed in the fuselage. It is powered by an Allison J-35 axial-flow turbojet power-plant, developing 4,000 pounds static, sea-level thrust. The fuel load of 250 gallons is transported in integral wing tanks. This aircraft is credited with the pioneer jet world-speed record of 650.6 miles per hour in level flight. This performance was attained over a standard 3 kilometer (1.86 mile) course. During the record flight, which was conducted at a temperature of 94° F., Mach 0.83 was attained.

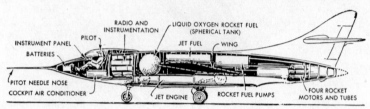

FIGURE 102. The Douglas "Skyrocket" Research Aircraft.

"Skyrocket"—A Swept-wing version of the Skystreak. Its length is somewhat greater, i.e., 45 feet, 3 inches. Wings are swept back at an angle of 35° and have a slight cathedral of 3°. Tail surfaces are swept back at an angle of 40°. Gross weight is 15,000 pounds. It is powered by a Westinghouse 24-C turbojet powerplant of 3,000 pounds thrust, and four Reaction Motors rocketjet powerplants which develop a total of 6,000 pounds thrust. Design speeds are of the order of 760 miles per hour at sea-level, and 660 miles per hour at 35,000 feet.

F3-D—(Skyknight) Naval Night-fighter Airplane. It is a large, two-place (side by side) aircraft, designed for carrier operations.

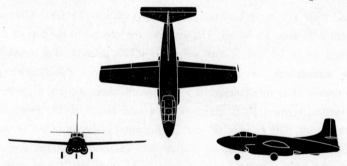

FIGURE 103. The Douglas F3-D "Skynight" Naval Fighter Airplane.

It is powered by two Westinghouse J-34 turbojet powerplants, mounted on either side of the fuselage under the wing roots. This aircraft is in the 600 mile per hour class. Its tactical altitude is well over 40,000 feet. The F3-D incorporates a tunnel escape hatch for use in emergency.

XF4-D—A Tailless Interceptor-fighter Aircraft. It is designed for catapulting from navy carrier decks for rapid climb to tactical altitude. It has a delta wing structure which is extended forward to accommodate the pilot's cockpit. No dimensional or performance data for this aircraft are available at present. It is designated the "Skyray."

A2-D—(Skyshark) Naval Attack Bomber. It is suitable for both tactical ground and sea-air attacks. It is powered by an Allison T-40 turboprop powerplant, developing 5,500 shaft horsepower, which drives two counterrotating "Aeroprop" propellers. The T-40 power-plant comprises two smaller units combined into a single engine. Such basic units may be combined into three or four, or even more,

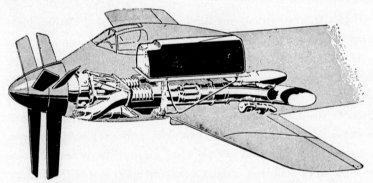

FIGURE 104. Powerplant Installation of the Douglas "A2D" Airplane.

powerplants, all of which are geared to rotate a single series of counter-rotating propellers. The performance characteristics of the A2-D are comparable to those of jet-powered fighters. The airplane can "hover" for ground support by cutting out one of its twin-turbine powerplant sections.

A3-D—Naval Attack Bomber. The configuration of this aircraft is of the swept-wing type, and it is twin turbojet powered. The powerplant utilized is the Westinghouse J-40-WE-6 Y-ducted turbojet, for which an output of 14,000 equivalent horsepower is claimed at operating air speeds. The United States Air Force is contemplating using this aircraft, in which event, it will carry the USAF designation of "RB-66." Subsequent naval versions will be powered by Pratt and Whitney J-57 split-compressor turbojet powerplants. The USAF versions will be powered by Allison J-71 turbojet units.

Model 1211-J—A Proposed, Four-engined, Swept-wing, Intercontinental Bombardment Aircraft. Gross take-off weight approximates 322,000 pounds. Design performance includes a maximum speed of over 450 knots, a normal absolute range of 11,000 nautical miles, and a combat altitude of 55,000 feet. The type of turboprop powerplants which will power this aircraft have not yet been decided on.

NORTH AMERICAN AVIATION INCORPORATED,
INGLEWOOD, CALIFORNIA

B-45—Multiple Jet-engined Bombardment Airplane. This is a high-wing monoplane with a tricycle landing gear. Wing span is 89 feet, 6 inches. Over-all length is 74 feet. Height from the ground to the top of the vertical fin is 25 feet. Gross weight approximates 82,000 pounds. According to the United States Air Force classification, this aircraft falls into the medium-bombardment-weight category. It is powered by four Allison, J-35, axial-flow, turbojet powerplants, providing a total of 16,000 pounds rated thrust. The powerplants are arranged in pairs in twin nacelles located on either side of the fuselage. Performance figures include a maximum speed of over 480 miles per hour, and a tactical radius of 800 miles. A ten-ton bomb load can be transported by the B-45. Pilot and copilot sit in tandem in the long, slender fuselage. The airplane is characterized by the complete absence of protruding members, such as gun turret "blisters."

FJ-1—Single-place, Carrier-based, Fighter Airplane. This is a low-wing monoplane with a tricycle landing gear. Wing span is 38 feet. 14¼ inches. Over-all length is 33 feet, 7⅞ inches. Over-all height

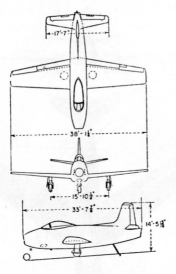

FIGURE 105. The North American FJ-1 Naval Fighter Airplane.

from the ground to the top of the vertical fin is 14 feet, 5 15/16 inches. Gross weight approximates 12,000 pounds. It is powered by a single Allison J-35 axial-flow turbojet powerplant. A single, continuous, straight-ram duct passes directly rearward to the turbojet compressor inlet from the air induction orifice located in the fuselage nose section. The wing structure is of the thin, laminar-flow type. The wing-tip fuel tanks are jettisonable. An unusual feature of this airplane is its bending nose-wheel strut, which enables the aircraft to "kneel down" while at rest. In this manner, carrier-deck space can be conserved, since the nose sections of succeeding aircraft can be stowed under the high empennage elements of the aircraft ahead. In addition, the heated jet exhaust blast is carried upward and away from the carrier deck during a runup or testing period.

F-86—United States Air Force Fighter-type Airplane. This is a considerably modified version of FJ-1. This model has swept-back wings and tail surfaces with the objective of increasing the critical speed of these members prior to encountering the adverse effects of

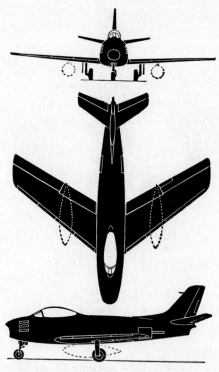

FIGURE 106. The North American F-86 "Sabrejet" Airplane.

compressibility. The over-all dimensions vary somewhat from those of the FJ-1, the wing span and the length both being 37 feet. The deep fuselage of the FJ-1 is replaced in the F-86 by a slimmer, low-drag structure. Its maximum speed approximates 630 miles per hour, thus yielding Mach 0.83. Operating ceiling is at 40,000 feet. An unusual feature of this airplane is its fuselage "dive brakes," consisting of large panels mounted flush on the rear fuselage section. They can be extended into the slip stream for creating heavy drag forces. The main purpose of these surfaces is to decelerate during high-speed flight maneuvers. Later models of the F-86 are powered by the General Electric J-47 turbojet powerplant, developing 6,000 pounds thrust with liquid injection. The latest Sabrejet fighter aircraft, designated the

"F-100" by USAF, incorporates a 45-degree swept-wing configuration, replacing the 35-degree swept-wing configuration of production models.

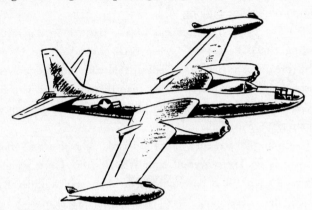

FIGURE 107. The North American B-45 "Tornado" Bombardment Airplane.

F-93—This aircraft is developed from, and is similar to, its predecessor, the F-86. However, the gross weight of this airplane approximates 10 tons, about twice that of the earlier design. Wing span is 39 feet. Over-all length is 44 feet. Height of the vertical fin above the ground is 16 feet. It is powered by the Pratt and Whitney J-48 powerplant, a redesigned version of the British Rolls-Royce "Tay" turbojet. This powerplant is rated at 6,250 pounds thrust, an additional 1,750 pounds being available by means of an afterburner. Flush air intakes are provided on either side of the fuselage, permitting the installation of elaborate radar equipment in the nose section. The large weight necessitates the provision of five landing-gear wheels. One wheel is located in the nose section, and two two-wheeled members are retractable into the wing panels.

F-95—An All-weather Interceptor-Fighter Airplane. It is modeled on the basic F-86 design. Wing span is 39 feet. Over-all length is 41 feet. It is powered by a General Electric J-47 turbojet powerplant, developing 5,200 pounds thrust. An afterburner boosts the thrust approximately 50 percent when short bursts of power are required. Since the F-95 is a single-place airplane, the pilot also operates the elaborate search radar equipment located in the nose section. A zero reader relieves a portion of the piloting load.

F-100—The Latest Development of the Basic F-86 Aircraft. The main wing panels have a 45° sweep back, instead of the 35° sweep back of previous models. A General Electric turbojet powerplant of considerably greater power output than that employed with former models is installed in the F-100. No dimensional or performance data of this aircraft are available.

AJ-1—Composite-powered, Carrier-based, Naval-attack Bomber. Wing span is 65 feet. Over-all length is 50 feet. Gross weight approximates 25 tons. It is powered by two Pratt and Whitney R-2800 piston engines, developing 2,300 horsepower each, plus a single, fuselage-mounted Allison J-33 turbojet powerplant. Maximum speed is 400 miles per hour. Radius of action is 1,200 miles. The AJ-1 is the largest and heaviest carrier-based aircraft. To expedite carrier stowage, the main wing members can be folded. In addition, the vertical fin folds to the right surface of the horizontal stabilizer. The AJ-1 is reportedly contemplated for atomic bomb operations. A newer, heavier version is planned to be powered by two Allison T-40 turbo-prop powerplants, in which, the turbojet unit would be eliminated.

FIGURE 108. The Northrop XF-79 "Flying Ram."

NORTHROP AIRCRAFT, INCORPORATED, HAWTHORNE, CALIFORNIA

YB-49—Multiple, Jet-engined Bombardment Airplane. This is a modification of the XB-35 "Flying Wing," which employed conventional reciprocating engines. It has a tailless, tapered wing structure. Its tricycle landing-gear assembly comprises a single nose wheel and heavy-duty dual main wheels. Wing span is 172 feet. Over-all length is 53 feet. Gross weight approximates 209,000 pounds. The weight, empty, is 88,100 pounds. It is powered by eight Allison J-35 axial-flow turbojet powerplants, providing a total of 32,000 pounds rated thrust. Performance figures include a maximum speed over 450 miles per hour and a range of 10,000 miles. A bomb and fuel load of about 60 tons can be transported by this long-range, heavy bombardment airplane. A special feature is the four dorsal fins mounted on the trailing edge of the wing. They function as air separators or dams in that they hinder the spilling of boundary layer air into the low-pressure region (created by the high-velocity air) aft of the turbojet powerplant banks. As a direct result of this arrangement, a straight-flow channel from the leading edge is obtained. A further feature is the electrically-operated throttle system which yields even and accurate jet power output.

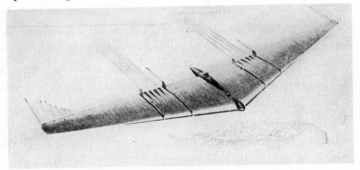

FIGURE 109. The Northrop YB-49 Bombardment Airplane.

XF-79—Single-place Fighter Airplane. It is also called the "Flying Ram." This is a tailless aircraft with tapered wings. The pilot flies in the prone position to eliminate "blackout" induced by accelerated flight maneuvers. Twin vertical stabilizers are mounted above the wing. Rudder assist ducts aid the operation of split-flap rudders located at the wing tips. Wing span is 38 feet. Other structural dimensions are not available. Tested performance indicates a speed of 525 miles per hour and a ceiling of 40,000 feet. This aircraft is primarily suitable for short-range interception.

X-4—Supersonic Research Aircraft. Wing span is 25 feet. Over-all length is 20 feet. Design gross weight is 7,000 pounds. Height from the ground to the top of the vertical fin is 15 feet. It is powered by two Westinghouse J-34 turbojet powerplants, one in each wing root. The mid-mounted wing member has a sharp sweep back. No horizontal fins or elevators are provided in this design. Both longitudinal and lateral control are effected by means of elevons mounted on the trailing edges of the wings. The resulting tail configuration is advantageous for the range, speed, and load-carrying properties because of its greatly reduced drag. Although one of the smallest jet-powered aircraft manufactured to date, the X-4 has very complete instrumentation.

F-89—Night Fighter Airplane. It is also designated the "Scorpion." Both the wing span and the over-all length approximate 50 feet. Gross weight is 30,000 pounds. It is powered by two Allison J-35 turbojet powerplants, rated at 4,000 pounds thrust each. Performance characteristics include a maximum range of 2,000 miles and a speed over 600 miles per hour when flying above the normal operating altitude of 40,-000 feet. The shoulder-mounted wing panels terminate in square tips. The sweep back is only a few degrees and insufficient to counteract the shock effects of compressibility encountered at transonic speed values. However, the swept-wing configuration prevents low landing speeds. This last is an essential requirement for all-weather fighter airplanes. It is very likely that this type of aircraft will be stationed at the outer perimeters of defense areas, which have usually short and otherwise inadequate runways. This explains the necessity for a practically straight wing in this fast, heavy aircraft. Maximum-span flaps are employed. The wing section is too thin to accommodate spoilers. As an alternate measure, "decelerons" are installed, which have split control surfaces and serve as ailerons, dive brakes, and landing-flap extensions. Large twin tailpipes are a feature of the F-89 airplane. These house the afterburners, which are responsible for much of the excellent performance of the aircraft.

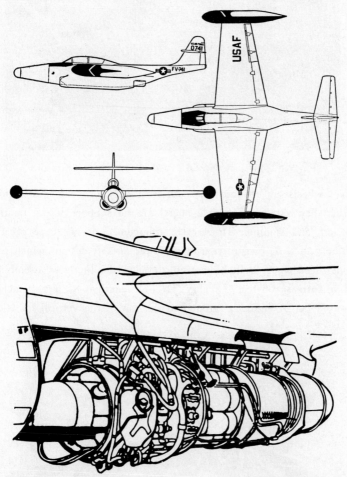

FIGURE 110. Northrop F-89D "Scorpion" Airplane with Wingtip Rocket Containers (Details of the Movable Engine Mount Are Shown).

MARTIN AIRCRAFT CORPORATION, BALTIMORE, MARYLAND

XB-48—Multiple Jet-engined Bombardment Airplane. A high-wing monoplane, with a bicycle-type landing gear. The main wheels are mounted fore and aft along the fuselage, into which they are retractable.

FIGURE 111. The Martin XB-48 Bombardment Airplane.

Small wheels are mounted beneath each engine-nacelle cluster, into which they retract, to provide lateral ground support during taxiing, take-off, and landing. The bicycle arrangement is necessary because of the thin wing construction of transonic aircraft designs which precludes deep wheel wells for housing retracted landing-gear assemblies. Wing span is 108 feet, 4 inches. Over-all length is 85 feet, 9 inches. Over-all height from the ground to the top of the vertical fin is 27

FIGURE 112.   The Martin B-51 Ground-support Aircraft.

feet, 6 inches. Weight (empty) is 58,500 pounds. According to the United States Air Force classification, this aircraft falls into the medium-bombardment-weight category. It is powered by six Allison J-35 axial-flow turbojet powerplants, providing a total of 24,000 pounds rated thrust. The jet powerplants are arranged in banks of three on either side of the fuselage. Its maximum speed is in the subsonic range. The Martin-designed wing of the XB-48 airplane is unusually thin.

B-51—Multiple Jet-engined Bombardment Airplane. Specially designed for short-range, tactical missions in support of ground-force units. Wing span is 55 feet. Over-all length is 80 feet. Height from ground level to the top of the vertical fin is 17 feet. Gross weight approximates 80,000 pounds. It is powered by three General Electric J-47 turbojet powerplants. These are installed in a rather unique arrangement, two units being located on fuselage pylons, and a third unit in the tail. Both the wing and tail assemblies of the B-51 airplane are swept back at an angle of 35°. The horizontal tail surfaces are mounted on top of the vertical stabilizer to form a T-shaped empennage assembly. The ailerons are replaced by spoilers, which effect lateral control. The variable-incidence wing member is also provided with leading edge slots. Classified in the light-bomber category, the B-51 is designed to accommodate a two-man crew. Equipment includes pilot-ejection seats, cabin pressurization, and air conditioning. Operation to and from small combat-area runways is anticipated. Therefore, the airplane is powered for faster starts. Four Aerojet JATO bottles are installed in the after portion of the fuselage to serve as take-off power assists. Conversely, in order to obtain lowered values of landing speed, a parachute is stowed in the after fuselage section to be released by the pilot when greater deceleration is required. Maximum sea-level speed of the B-51 airplane is of the order of 650 miles per hour. This performance approximates Mach 0.86.

P4M-1—Long-range Patrol, Bombing, and Torpedo-carrying Aircraft. It features composite powerplants housed in two nacelles. Each nacelle accommodates a Pratt and Whitney R-4360 piston engine of

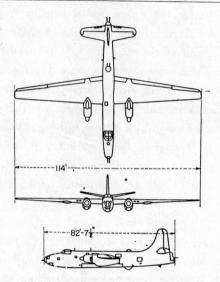

FIGURE 113. The Martin P4M-1 Long-range Naval Patrol Bomber.

3,000 horsepower, plus a General Electric J-33-4 turbojet powerplant, developing 4,000 pounds static thrust. Gross weight is 80,681 pounds, including an 8,000-pound bomb load. A crew of ten is carried. Range is 2,940 miles. High speed is 398 miles per hour, when utilizing both reciprocating engines and jet powerplants.

McDonnell Aircraft Corporation, St. Louis, Missouri

FH-1 (Phantom)—Single-place Carrier-based Fighter Airplane. This is a low-wing monoplane, with a tricycle landing gear. Wing span is 40 feet, 9½ inches. Over-all length is 37 feet, 2½ inches. Gross weight is just under 10,000 pounds. It is powered by two six-stage, axial-flow Westinghouse 19-B turbojet powerplants, providing a total of 2,800 pounds static sea-level thrust. Performance figures include a maximum speed of over 500 miles per hour, a service ceiling of 37,000 feet, and a range of 1,000 miles. An unusual feature of the FH-1 is its thickened wing roots in which are housed the turbojet powerplants. Ingenious design made possible the utilization of the root section as an airfoil. In addition, it provides greater wing-spar depth at the location where it is most effective. The FH-1 was originally designated as the FD-1. This symbol was later changed to avoid confusion with aircraft manufactured by the Douglas Aircraft Company.

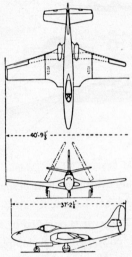

FIGURE 114. The McDonnell "Phantom" Naval Fighter Airplane.

F2H-1 (Banshee)—A Larger, Modified Version of FH-1. Its gross weight is 14,000 pounds. Performance figures include a maximum speed of over 600 miles per hour and a rate of climb of 9,000 feet per minute. Special features of the McDonnell aircraft are folding wings and bending nose-wheel struts, both of which expedite carrier stowage. In addition, the bending struts permit the heated, jet exhaust blast to be carried upward and away from the carrier deck during a run-up or testing period. The Westinghouse J-34-WE-30 powerplants of the F2H-1 airplane have approximately twice the design power output of those selected for the FH-1 aircraft. The larger powerplants have eleven stages of axial compression and two turbine stages. Wing-tip fuel tanks on the F2H-1 airplane allow the transportation of 4,800 gallons of fuel. This is the greatest fuel load carried by any naval jet-propelled design.

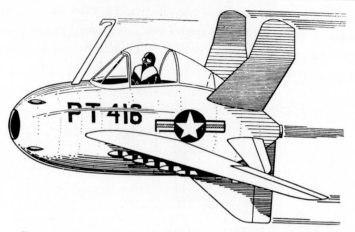

FIGURE 115. The McDonnell XF-85 "Goblin" Parasite Fighter.

XF-85—Parasite Fighter Airplane. It is designed for launching and recovery aboard the B-36 bombardment aircraft. Wing span is 21 feet. Over-all length is 15 feet. It is powered by a single Westinghouse 24-C axial-flow turbojet powerplant, developing 3,000 pounds static thrust. In outline, it is a stubby, barrel-shaped craft which streamlines the Westinghouse powerplant. The XF-85 is stowed in a B-36 bomb bay with its wings folded; the unfolding occurs as the aircraft is dropped for launching. Estimated speed is over 650 miles per hour. It can operate at an altitude of 45,000 feet. Its distinctive feature is its very high rate of climb, which was much greater than that of any contemporary fighter aircraft. A drawback of the XF-85 lies in the difficulty of retrieving the aircraft when its small amount of fuel is exhausted. Should combat conditions continue during the retrieving process, a bomber which slows down to "latch on" to a spent fighter places itself in dire jeopardy.

XF-88—Single-place Penetration Fighter Airplane. Wing span is 40 feet. Gross weight is 15,000 pounds. It is powered by two Westinghouse J-34 turbojet powerplants. Wings are swept back at a 35° angle. Cabin pressurization is provided. It is designed to operate deep inside enemy territory, either as a fighter-bomber or as a bomber escort. Many data regarding this airplane are still withheld. An experimental installation incorporates an Allison T-38 turboprop powerplant mounted in the nose of an F-88 airplane and rotating a Curtiss supersonic propeller through a special gearbox. The two J-34 turbojet powerplants are retained in the installation. Performance through the transsonic range is anticipated by the use of the combined powerplant arrangement. The F-88 may become the first propeller-driven supersonic aircraft. The twin-jet swept-wing "XF-88A" "Voodoo" has now undergone certain structural modifications which have caused it to be designated the "F-101" by USAF.

FIGURE 116. The McDonnell F-88 "Voodoo" Fighter (Redesignated F-101).

XF3H-1—Carrier-based Fighter Airplane. This newest McDonnell model of advanced design has a needle-nose. Its performance, which is said to be phenomenal, has not been disclosed by the Bureau of Aeronautics, Navy Department. It is also designated the "Demon."

RYAN AERONAUTICAL COMPANY, SAN DIEGO, CALIFORNIA

FR-1 (Fireball)—Single-place, Carrier-based, Naval Fighter Airplane. This is a low-wing monoplane, with a tricycle landing gear.

Wing span is 40 feet. Over-all length is 32 feet, 4 inches. Height from the ground to the top of the vertical fin is 12 feet, 4 inches. Gross weight approximates 9,862 pounds. A composite-engined aircraft, powered jointly by a Wright R-1820 reciprocating engine, developing 1,350 horsepower, mounted in the nose, and a General Electric J-31 centrifugal-flow turbojet powerplant, mounted in the fuselage, aft of the pilot's cockpit. Both the conventional piston engine and the jet powerplant utilize the same fuel, thus eliminating the requirement for a dual fuel system. Performance figures include a maximum speed of 300 miles per hour on either engine singly, and over 425 miles per hour with both powerplants operative. Rate of climb approximates 5,000 feet per minute.

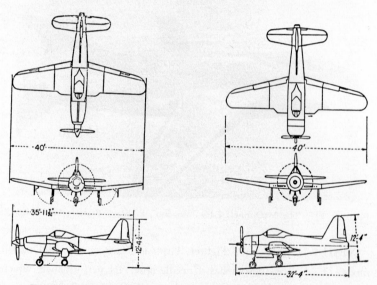

FIGURE 117. Two Versions of the Ryan Naval Fighter Aircraft.

F2R-1—This aircraft is essentially similar to the FR-1. However, a General Electric T-31 turboprop powerplant, rotating a four-bladed Hamilton Standard propeller, replaces the conventional reciprocating engine in the nose section. The over-all length and height are slightly greater, i.e., 35 feet, 11 7/32 inches and 12 feet, 4¼ inches, respectively.

The maximum speed is over 500 miles per hour. Although the airframe structure is basically identical with that of the FR-1, the increased torque has necessitated additional vertical stabilizer area on the F2R-1 airplane.

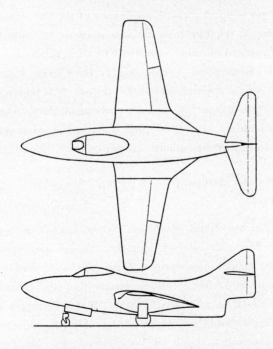

FIGURE 118. The Grumman F9F "Panther" Naval Fighter.

GRUMMAN AIRCRAFT ENGINEERING CORPORATION, BETHPAGE, L.I., NEW YORK

F9F (Panther)—Naval Shipboard Fighter Aircraft. It is powered by a redesigned Rolls-Royce "Nene" centrifugal-flow turbojet powerplant, equipped with water injection and tail-pipe afterburning facilities. This powerplant unit is produced in quantity in the United States by Pratt and Whitney and is designated the J-42. Its performance is characterized by a short (450-foot) take-off run, suitable for carrier decks. This is accomplished by four blower doors which induce an accelerated air flow through the turbojet plenum chamber. In this manner, a high-energy air flow is provided at moderately low values of airplane forward velocity, yielding maximum values of static thrust for take-off. Wing-nose flaps, together with the previously mentioned blower doors, provide for lowered landing speeds of the order of 80 to 85 miles per hour. A characteristic feature of the F9F airplane is its tail configuration resulting from the installation of an unusually short tail pipe. Estimated maximum speed is 650 miles per hour.

XF10F-1—Single-place, Swept-wing, Naval Carrier Fighter Aircraft. Gross weight approximates 31,000 pounds. It is powered by the improved Westinghouse J-40 turbojet powerplant, developing 10,000 pounds rated thrust. Maximum speed is reportedly about 800 miles per hour. No further dimensional and performance data are available.

CHANCE VOUGHT AIRCRAFT CORPORATION, STRATFORD, CONNECTICUT

F6U-1 (Pirate)—Naval, Shipboard, Fighter Aircraft. It is powered by a single Westinghouse 24-C axial-flow turbojet powerplant, producing 3,000 pounds rated thrust. Wing span is 32 feet, 6 inches. Over-all length is 37 feet, 7 inches. Height from the ground to the top of the vertical fin is 11 feet, 9 inches. Weight (empty) is 7,560 pounds. Weight (loaded) is 11,300 pounds. Service ceiling is 38,000 feet. It is constructed largely of Vought-developed "Metalite" sandwich material for exterior smoothness. Wing-tip fuel tanks are designed to spring clear on release, preventing the possibility of their fouling the tail members. Maximum speed is over 500 miles per hour.

FIGURE 119. The Chance-Vought F7U-1 "Cutlass" Naval Fighter.

F7U-1 (Cutlass)—Twin Jet-engined, Naval, Fighter Airplane. A tailless aircraft, in which two vertical stabilizers, with attached rudders, are located at the trailing edges of the main wing members. The wings are swept back at a 45° angle. It is powered by two Westinghouse J-34 turbojet powerplants. Maximum speed is over 650 miles per hour. Operational altitude is 40,000 feet. Extensive use has been made of magnesium alloy. Lightweight "sandwich" materials predominate in its construction. "Ailevators," combining the functions of elevator and aileron members are provided with hydraulic boost to overcome the forces induced by high-speed flight. In addition to the hydraulic controls, equipment includes elaborate radio devices, navigational aids, instrumentation, and cabin pressurization. A newly-developed "short" afterburner is an item of standard equipment.

FOREIGN JET-PROPELLED AIRCRAFT

BRITISH AIRCRAFT

Gloster "Meteor"—Clipped Wing Monoplane Fighter Airplane. It is powered by two Rolls-Royce "Derwent V" turbojet powerplants, providing a total of 7,000 pounds rated thrust. Gross weight is 14,450 pounds. Wing area is 350 square feet. Normal wing loading is 41.4 pounds per square foot. Performance figures include a maximum speed of 580 miles per hour, a rate of climb of 7,800 feet per minute, and a service ceiling approximating 50,000 feet. Normal range is 910 miles.

FIGURE 120. A British Jet-propelled Aircraft, the Gloster Turbojet Fighter (Powered by a Single Whittle Centrifugal-flow Unit).

An all-weather, night-fighter version is designated NF.11. It differs from the original type primarily in the configuration of the nose section, which is considerably elongated in order to accommodate elaborate, air-borne, interception radar equipment. Two newer versions of the Meteor are in production. One is powered by twin Rolls-Royce "Avon" axial-flow turbojet powerplants of 6,250 pounds thrust each. Improved performance figures for this aircraft include a rate of climb of 10,000 feet per minute. A still more recent model is powered by the Armstrong-Siddeley "Sapphire" turbojet powerplant, which develops 7,200 pounds thrust and is probably one of the most powerful aircraft turbojet powerplants in existence.

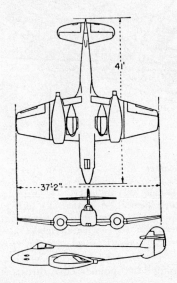

FIGURE 121. The Gloster "Meteor" Fighter Airplane.

Gloster "E. 1/44"—Single-place Fighter. It is powered by a single Rolls-Royce "Nene" turbojet powerplant, developing 5,000 pounds thrust. Air intake is accomplished by means of twin "Nostril" inlet ducts. Wing span is 36 feet. Over-all length is 38 feet. Height from the ground to the top of the vertical fin is 11 feet, 8 inches. Total wing area is 254 square feet, of which the flap area represents 30.5 square feet.

De Havilland "Swallow"—Research Aircraft. Built with sharply swept-back wings and a short, stubby fuselage. It is constructed entirely of metal and equipped with a retractable tricycle landing gear. Originally, it was fitted with fixed leading-edge slots; new models have autoslots. It is powered by a single De Havilland "Goblin" turbojet

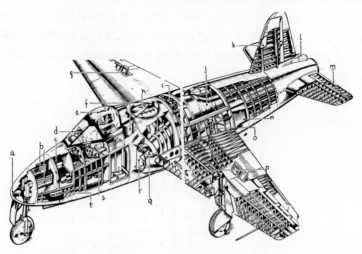

FIGURE 122. *The Gloster "E. 1/44" Fighter:* (a) cockpit ventilating pipe; (b) batteries; (c) radio; (d) windshield de-icing; (e) electrically operated hood; (f) front fuselage fuel tank; (g) air brakes; (h) main fuel tank; (i) auxiliary gearbox; (j) Rolls-Royce Nene 1 jet engine; (k) surface aerial; (l) tail parachute; (m) elevator-trim tab; (n) rear-fuselage fuel tanks; (o) hydraulic reservoir; (p) dive recovery flap; (q) engine air intake duct; (r) boundary-layer bleeder duct; (s) main electric panel; (t) pneumatic air container.

powerplant, developing 3,000 pounds rated thrust. Performance figures include a maximum speed over 600 miles per hour.

De Havilland "Vampire"—Twin Outrigger Monoplane Fighter Aircraft. It is a standard Royal Air Force tactical aircraft. It is powered by a single De Havilland "Goblin" Turbojet powerplant, developing 3,000 pounds rated thrust. It is of composite wood and metal construction. Performance figures include a maximum speed of 540 miles per hour, a rate of climb of 4,250 feet per minute, and a service ceiling of 51,000 feet. Normal range is 1,050 miles.

Later model Vampires, designated, respectively, Mk. V and Mk. VI, are specially strengthened, high-performance, assault versions of the original type. Improvements include shortened and stiffened wings, heavier landing-gear members to absorb underwing loads, and a braced fuselage tank to withstand severe pull-out shock loads. Power

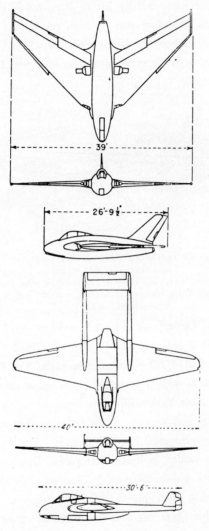

FIGURE 123. Two de Havilland Jet-powered Designs.

is furnished by an improved Rolls-Royce "Goblin III" turbojet power-plant rated at 3,300 pounds thrust. Maximum speed and range are 531 miles per hour and 1,145 miles, respectively. A naval model is the Mk.22, designated as the "Sea Vampire." In this aircraft, carrier-approach runs are controlled by lift spoilers, rather than by throttle movements. This procedure permits high revolutions per minute to be maintained throughout the landing procedure, instantaneous power being thus available in the event of a wave-off signal from the carrier deck.

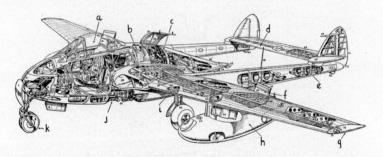

FIGURE 124. *The De Havilland Mk.22 "Sea Vampire" Navy Fighter:*
(a) pressure cabin; (b) main tank; (c) easy access to engine; (d) latest low-position tailplane; (e) metal tail booms; (f) extended dive brakes; (g) clipped tip; (h) long range wing tank; (i) accelerator hook; (j) four cannon; (k) strengthened nose wheel.

De Havilland "Comet"—The First Pure-jet-powered Airline Transport in the World. It is powered by four De Havilland "Ghost" turbojet powerplants, rated at 5,000 pounds thrust each. The Comet was designed to operate at 40,000 feet and to transport twenty passengers from London to New York within five and one-half hours. This objective necessitates performance of the order of 500 miles per hour. Gross weight approximates 100,000 pounds. Actual take-offs have been made, fully loaded, within 1,100 yards. Empty take-offs have been accomplished within 500 yards. The Comet is said to be considerably less noisy than piston-engined transports. One possible explanation for this phenomenon is that the cone of sound from each of the inboard turbojet pods just misses the passenger cabin. The chief sources of noise are the enormous masses of air slipping past the cabin at high velocity. A feature of the Comet is the "redux" method of molecular welding employed in its fabrication. By means of this method, large-area metal panels were stiffened without rivets.

Supermarine "E.10/44"—A jet-powered modification of the piston-engined "Spiteful." It is an all-metal monoplane; one of the few jet-powered aircraft which have a two-wheel landing gear. It is powered by a single Rolls-Royce "Nene" centrifugal-flow turbojet powerplant, developing 5,000 pounds rated thrust. Performance figures include a maximum speed of over 500 miles per hour.

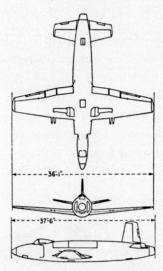

FIGURE 125. Supermarine Jet-powered Aircraft.

Vickers-Armstrong, Ltd., manufacturers of the Supermarine E.10/44, have designated a later version the "Sea Attacker." Although performance in the 590 miles per hour category has been attained by this aircraft, it is felt by the Royal Air Force and the British Ministry of Supply that the power output of the Rolls-Royce Nene turbojet has not been fully utilized. It is highly probable that some form of supersonic, swept-wing configuration will replace the tapered-wing structure.

Supermarine "535"—Single-place Fighter Aircraft. Vickers-Armstrong engineers designed this airplane with more sweep back than found in any other contemporary British fighter airplane. Wing span is 31 feet, 8 inches. Over-all length is 42 feet, 11 inches. Height from

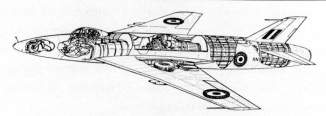

FIGURE 126. The Supermarine "535" Jet-powered Aircraft.

the ground to the top of the vertical fin is 12 feet, 6 inches. It is powered by a Rolls-Royce Nene turbojet powerplant, developing 5,000 pounds thrust. An afterburner is attached. Although performance figures are not available, a high Mach number may be assumed. Unusual features of the Supermarine 535 include a tail wheel, added to its retractable tricycle main landing gear. Very large wing flaps constitute another noteworthy feature.

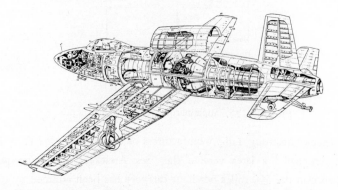

FIGURE 127. The Vickers-Armstrong "Sea Attacker" Navy Fighter.

Saunders-Roe "SR-A-1"—A Single-place Jet-powered Flying-boat Fighter. It is powered by two Metropolitan-Vickers "F 2/4" "Beryl" axial-flow turbojet powerplants, providing a total of 7,000 pounds rated thrust. The powerplants are submerged within the central hull. A large, elliptical air-induction scoop is located in the nose section and is equipped with a water trap for rough-sea handling. Semiretractable wing floats are swung inboard during flight. It has a pressurized cabin and a pilot-ejector seat. Performance figures include a maximum design speed of 500 miles per hour and a landing speed of 100 miles per hour.

FIGURE 128. The Vickers-Armstrong "Attacker" Fighter.

An advanced version of this aircraft is the Saro "S.R/45" single-place, flying-boat fighter. It is powered also by twin Metrovick "Beryl" axial-flow turbojet powerplants. This aircraft mounts four-cannon armament. It is outfitted for, and intended to be employed in, Far-East areas.

Saunders-Roe "Dutchess"—A Seventy-four passenger Turbojet-powered Flying Boat. Wing span is 135 feet. Over-all length is 124 feet. Gross weight is 130,000 pounds. Maximum payload is 21,000 pounds. It is powered by six de Havilland "Ghost" turbojet power-plants, rated at 5,000 pounds thrust each. Maximum level speed is 550 miles per hour. Most economical cruising speed is 468 miles per hour. Operating altitude is 30,000 feet. Equivalent still-air range

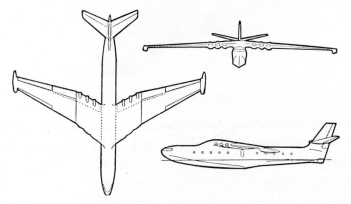

FIGURE 129. The Saunders-Roe "Dutchess" Flying Boat.

is 3,100 miles. Interesting features of the Dutchess are adjustable-pitch wing-tip floats and a split water rudder.

Saunders-Roe "Princess"—A One-hundred-passenger, Turboprop-jet-powered Flying Boat. Larger than the Dutchess, this aircraft has been designed with ease of maintenance as a primary objective. Gross weight is 300,000 pounds. It is powered by ten Bristol "Proteus" turbo-propjet powerplants, developing 3,200 shaft horsepower plus 800 pounds static thrust each. Design cruising speed is 380 miles per hour. Operating altitude is 37,000 feet. The Princess is designed to operate over a 3,500 mile range. This indicates an equivalent still-air range of approximately 5,500 miles. Dimensions of the original model, which is designated the "SR-45," include a wing span of 220 feet and an over-all length of 146 feet. The Proteus turbopropjet powerplants are arranged in such a manner as to include four coupled installations (developing 6,400 equivalent shaft horsepower each) plus two single engines located in outboard nacelles. Each powerplant drives six-bladed, contra-rotating propellers.

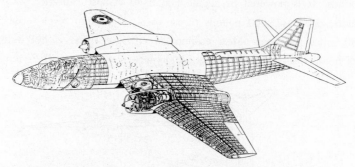

FIGURE 130. The English Electric "Canberra" Light Bomber.

English Electric Company "Canberra"—Short-range Bombardment Aircraft. Wing span is 64 feet. Over-all length is 65 feet, 6 inches. Height of the vertical fin above ground level is 15 feet, 7 inches. Track is 15 feet, 5 inches. It is powered by two Rolls-Royce "Avon" turbojet powerplants. These newly developed, axial-flow turbojet powerplants are rated at 7,500 pounds static thrust each. This figure represents one of the highest recorded outputs among turbojet engines. This gives a power loading of three. Tactical radius is 400 to 500 miles. Operational altitude is 50,000 feet. There is no American counterpart of the Canberra. According to United States tactical standards, an aircraft of its general specifications is not large enough to be classified as a light bomber. The Canberra most nearly approximates the Northrop F-89 "Scorpion," a two-place, all-weather fighter. A very recent version of the original design, designated as the Mk.2, has a modified nose section. Provision is also made for a third crew member. The Canberra is now contemplated for employment as a night intruder by United States Air Force. Its USAF designation is "B-57A." The American version will be powered by two Curtiss-Wright-built Armstrong-Siddeley Sapphire turbojet powerplants, developing 7,200 pounds thrust each.

Hawker "P.1081"—Single-place Fighter Aircraft. This is an improvement over two earlier models, the P.1040 and the P.1052. Wing span is 31 feet, 6 inches. Over-all length is 37 feet, 4 inches. It is powered by a Rolls-Royce Nene turbojet powerplant, producing 5,000 pounds thrust. Estimated low-level speed is over 650 miles per hour. It has swept wings and tail surfaces. Its single tail-pipe exhaust system is a distinct departure from previous Hawker practice which had bifurcated, or split, tail-pipe members. The Hawker P.1081 is noted for its excellent maneuverability, both at high and low altitudes.

Another advanced type is the Hawker N.7/47 naval fighter. It is powered by the Rolls-Royce Nene and is in the 600 miles per hour category. Its design represents a return to conventional Hawker configurations, since the single turbojet powerplant is provided with twin wing-root air ducts and two separate exhaust outlets. It is also designated the "Sea Hawk."

Armstrong-Whitworth "52"—Tailless Jet-powered Research Aircraft. Wing span is 90 feet. Gross weight is 30,000 pounds. Normal wing loading is 25.1 pounds per square foot. It is powered by two Rolls-Royce Nene centrifugal-flow turbojet powerplants, providing a

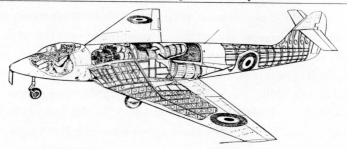

FIGURE 131. The Hawker P.1052 Fighter Aircraft.

total of 10,000 pounds rated thrust. A feature of this aircraft is its method of boundary layer control. Autoflaps, located within the turbo air-intake orifices, create the requisite suction for this purpose.

Armstrong-Whitworth "AW 55"—Designated the "Apollo," this is a transport aircraft, seating twenty-four to thirty passengers. Wing area is 840 square feet. Gross weight approximates 36,500 pounds. Maximum speed is 360 miles per hour. Cruising speed is 320 miles per hour. Normal range is over 1,000 miles. It is powered by four Armstrong-Siddeley "Mamba" turbopropjet powerplants, developing

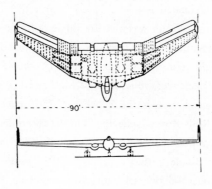

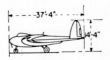

FIGURE 132. The Armstrong-Whitworth Research Aircraft.

1,010 shaft horsepower plus 367 pounds thrust each. The aircraft is constructed entirely of metal. The fuselage is truly circular.

Vickers "VC-2"—Designated the "Viceroy," this is a transport aircraft seating twenty-four to thirty-two passengers. Wing area is 885 square feet. Gross weight approximates 38,650 pounds. Maximum speed is 375 miles per hour. Cruising speed is 275 miles per hour. It is powered by four Armstrong-Siddeley "Mamba" turbopropjet powerplants, developing 1,010 shaft horsepower plus 367 pounds thrust each.

A somewhat larger version of this transport is the Vickers "Viscount." This is a forty-seat airliner. It is powered by four Rolls-Royce "Dart" turboprop powerplants, developing 1,400 shaft horsepower each. The cruising speed of the Viscount is over 300 miles per hour. This is the first turboprop-powered transport to be utilized in actual scheduled airline operations. A modified version of the Viscount has been fitted with two Rolls-Royce "Tay" turbojet powerplants, developing 6,250 pounds thrust each. The modified aircraft is to be employed for high-altitude research.

Bristol—"175"—Turboprop-powered Transport Aircraft. Wing

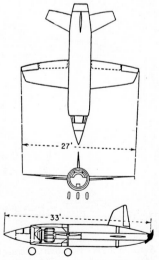

FIGURE 133. The Miles Supersonic Aircraft.

span is 140 feet. Over-all length is 114 feet. Height from ground level to the top of the vertical fin is 36 feet, 8 inches. Wheel tread is 31 feet. Total wing area is 2,055 square feet. It is powered by four Bristol Proteus turboprop powerplants, developing 3,200 shaft horse-

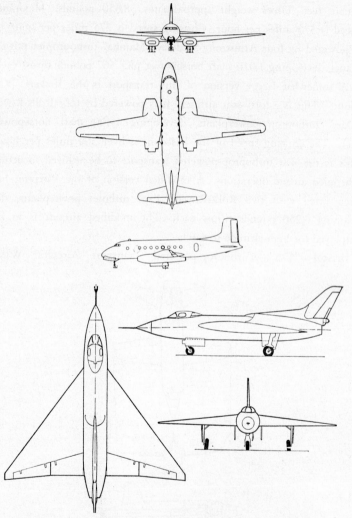

FIGURE 134. The Avro "Ashton" Research Aircraft; The Avro "707-B" Delta-wing Research Aircraft.

power each. Fuel capacity is 6,950 U.S. gallons. Performance data for this aircraft are not available.

Handley Page "Hermes"—The "Hermes 4" is an airline transport which seats forty to seventy passengers. It is powered by four Bristol "Theseus" turbopropjet powerplants, developing 2,200 shaft horsepower plus 590 pounds rated thrust each. Cruising speed is 283 miles per hour. Gross weight approximates 82,000 pounds. The "Hermes Mk.5" is a later, improved model, which cruises at 349 miles per hour.

Great Britain is engaged in the development of a series of turbopropjet-powered tactical aircraft. A brief description of the prominent types follows:

Westland "T.F.2"—Single-place Strike Fighter. It is powered by a single Armstrong-Siddeley "Python" turbopropjet powerplant, developing 3,670 shaft horsepower plus 1,150 pounds rated thrust. The powerplant drives an eight-bladed, contra-rotating propeller. The aircraft's high-lift wing flaps are extended for take-off.

Blackburn "Y.A.5"—Single-place Naval Strike Fighter. An extension of the piston-engined "Firecrest" strike single-seater. It is turbopropjet powered. A structural feature is its pronounced gull wing.

Fairey "17"—Antisubmarine Aircraft. It is powered by an Armstrong-Siddeley "Double Mamba" turbopropjet powerplant, rotating coaxial propellers. It is noted for its excellent visibility, which is a major consideration in carrier-based aircraft. The Fairey 17 incorporates a novel wing-folding system. Each wing panel breaks in two places to facilitate stowage aboard limited carrier installations. An unusual feature is its retractable radar equipment.

Short "S.B.3"—Antisubmarine Aircraft. It is powered by two Armstrong-Siddeley "Mamba" turbopropjet powerplants, developing 1,010 shaft horsepower plus 367 pounds rated thrust each. It is also called "Dumbo." This aircraft is actually a jet-powered adaptation of the carrier-based "Sturgeon."

Boulton Paul "T.1"—Military Trainer. Its design conforms to the Royal Air Force's recent three-seat trainer policy. Wing span is 39

feet, 4 inches. Over-all length is 36 feet, 6 inches. Gross weight is
7,795 pounds. Maximum speed is 307 miles per hour at the operational
altitude of 20,000 feet. Service ceiling is 36,750 feet. This aircraft is
called the "Balliol," and, with its counterpart, the Avro "Athenea," is
designed to accommodate various makes of turbopropjet powerplants,
including the Armstrong-Siddeley "Mamba," The Rolls-Royce "Dart,"
and the Napier "Naiad."

The following are a few outstanding types of British research aircraft.

Miles "E 24/43" "Supersonic"—Composite Jet-powered Research
Aircraft. It is powered by a triple-stage propulsion unit designed by
Power Jets, Ltd., of England. The first stage comprises a centrifugal-
flow turbojet powerplant. The ejected, hot exhaust gases are directed
to a second turbine which functions as a ducted fan. The resultant mixture flows to an athoyd powerplant which gives the third power stage.

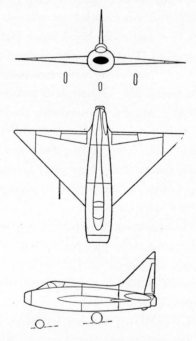

FIGURE 135. The Boulton Paul "P.111" Delta-winged Research Aircraft.

The estimated horsepower of the combined powerplants is 17,000. Anticipated performance includes a maximum speed of 1,000 miles per hour.

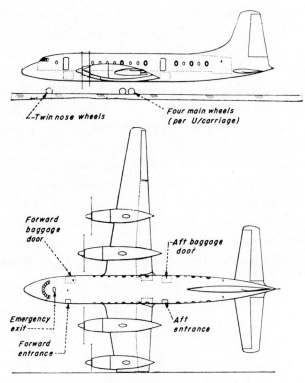

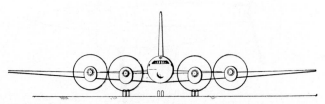

FIGURE 136. The Bristol "175" Transport Aircraft.

Avro "707B"—Delta-winged Research Aircraft. Wing span is 33 feet. Wing leading edge is swept back at an angle of 52°. Total wing area is 363 square feet. Gross weight approximates 8,000 pounds. Performance figures are not available. It is powered by a Rolls-Royce "Derwent" powerplant.

Another Avro research aircraft is the "Ashton 1." This is a transport airplane, developed from its "Tudor" predecessor. Several modifications have been made, however, to properly equip the "Ashton 1" for its role as a research transport. These include a new tricycle landing gear, redesigned nose section, and a squared-off vertical stabilizer member. It is powered by four Rolls-Royce Nene turbojet powerplants, developing a total of 20,000 pounds rated thrust. The powerplants are grouped in two underslung nacelles.

Supermarine "Swift"—Research Aircraft. Characterized by sharply swept-back wings and tail surfaces. It is a modification of the standard tactical Supermarine "Attacker" fighter aircraft. It is powered by a single Rolls-Royce Nene centrifugal-flow turbojet powerplant.

Boulton Paul "P.111"—Delta-winged Research Aircraft. Wing span is 33 feet, 6 inches. Over-all length is 26 feet, 1 inch. Height from

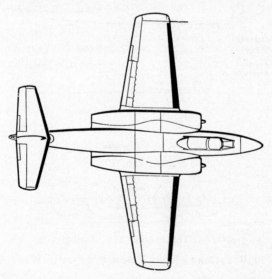

FIGURE 137. The Avro-Canada CF-100 "Canuck" Fighter.

the ground to the top of the vertical fin is 12 feet, 6 inches. Wing leading edge is swept back approximately 45°. Trailing edge is straight. It is powered by a single Rolls-Royce Nene turbojet powerplant, developing 5,000 pounds rated thrust. Engine air is admitted through a bifurcated inlet duct. The airplane is equipped with a pilot-ejection seat.

There is a distinct trend in Great Britain toward the development of four-engined jet bombardment aircraft. Four impressive versions are in various phases of production from the design stages to actual flight-testing. The Vickers "660" is a swept-wing design, powered by four Rolls-Royce Avon turbojet powerplants buried in the wing roots. It has a maximum speed of about 630 miles per hour, and a ceiling of 55,000 feet. The Short "S.A.4" is powered by four Rolls-Royce Avon turbojet powerplants mounted in pairs, one superimposed on the other. It has a 4-wheeled bogie landing gear. A crew of five is carried. Avro and Handley-Page also have four-jet-engined bomber design, details of which are not available.

CANADIAN AIRCRAFT

A.V. Roe, Canada, Ltd. "CF-100"—Two-place, Long-range, All-weather Fighter Aircraft. Wing span is 52 feet. Over-all length is 52 feet, 6 inches. Height from ground level to the top of the cockpit canopy is 10 feet, 7 inches. Height to the top of the vertical stabilizer is 15 feet, 1 inch. The horizontal stabilizer has a length of 21 feet and is mounted high on the vertical fin. The cockpit of the airplane is fitted with two Martin-Baker pilot-ejection seats. The original model is powered by two Rolls-Royce "Avon" axial-flow turbojet powerplants, developing 6,250 pounds rated thrust each. It is planned to power later models with an improved version of Avro Canada's "Chinook" turbojet powerplant. This axial-flow turbojet is constructed at the Toronto plant. The existing version is designed to produce 2,590 pounds thrust at 10,000 revolutions per minute. An even later development is the Avro Canada "Orenda," officially rated at over 6,000 pounds thrust. This powerplant will probably be finally installed in the aircraft which is designated the "Canuck."

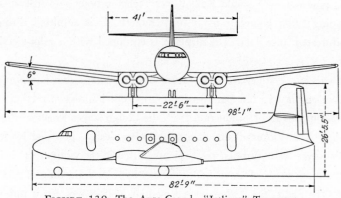

FIGURE 138. The Avro-Canada "Jetliner" Transport.

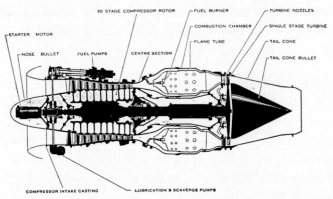

FIGURE 139. The Canadian "Orenda" Turbojet Powerplant.

A.V. Roe, Canada, Ltd. "Jetliner"—Airline Transport Aircraft. It seats forty to fifty passengers. For high-density application, sixty passengers can be accommodated. Wing span is 98 feet, 1 inch. Overall length is 82 feet, 9 inches. Height from the ground to the top of the vertical fin is 26 feet, 5.5 inches. It cruises at 400 miles per hour at 6,000 feet altitude. Cruise operations are conducted at 14,000 revolutions per minute. Take-off is accomplished at 14,700 revolutions per minute. It is powered by four Rolls-Royce "Derwent 5" turbojet powerplants, developing 3,500 pounds static thrust each at sea level. The powerplants are housed in pairs in twin underslung nacelles which also house the main landing wheels. Later models of the Jetliner may also be powered by the Improved Canadian Chinook turbojet power-plant.

AUSTRALIAN AIRCRAFT

Undesignated Single-place Experimental (Fighter) Aircraft. It is constructed by the Government Aircraft Factory, Fisherman's Bend, Victoria and tested at the Woomera Rocket Range in South Australia. A missile-type airplane, with a sharp, straight wing and favorable subsonic speed characteristics. Being very small, it is readily adaptable to high production. No dimensional or performance data are avail-able. It is powered by a single Armstrong-Siddeley "Adder" turbojet powerplant, developing 1,000 pounds thrust. This is a so-called "baby turbojet," a development of the "Mamba" unit.

FRENCH AIRCRAFT

SO-6000—Two-place, jet-powered Research Aircraft. This is a monoplane of all-metal construction which is distinguished by its ex-tremely wide-tread, hydraulically retractable, tricycle landing gear. Gross weight is 8,820 pounds. Total wing area is 150.6 square feet. Wing loading approaches 50 pounds per square foot. The original design was powered by a single Rateau "A-65" turbojet powerplant, developing 1,763 pounds rated thrust. Several prototypes are in the design stage, all of which are to be powered by different types of turbo-jet powerplants. Prominent manufacturers of aircraft turbojet power-plants in France include, in addition to Rateau, the Compagnie Electro Mécanique, the Société Turbomeca, and Atar. Most of the members of Atar are German technicians of the former Bayreusch Motoren Werke. The SO-6000 is the product of S.N.C.A.S.O. (Société Nationale de Constructions Aéronautique du Sud-Ouest), one of several French nationalized companies.

Several improved modifications of the SO-6000 are being flight tested. The SO-6020 "Espadon" single-jet-engined fighter is one of these. It was built originally with the air-intake duct suspended below the after fuselage section. A newer type, designated "SO-6021," has side inlets. The "SO-6025" design reverts back to the fuselage belly duct arrangement. However, only the forward portion of the housing is utilized as the air-intake duct. The after portion serves to accommodate a rocket unit.

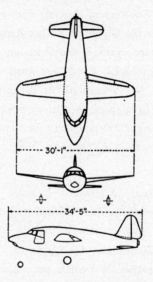

FIGURE 140. The French "SO-6000" Research Aircraft.

SO-M2—Experimental Sonic-flight Research Aircraft. This model is a half-scale version of the original "SO-4000," itself an experimental, two-place, twin-jet-engined bomber, powered by Hispano-Suiza Nene centrifugal-flow turbojet powerplants. The M2 aircraft has swept wings and is powered by a single Rolls-Royce Derwent V turbojet powerplant. Maximum speed is 1,000 kilometers per hour (621 miles per hour). A feature of the airplane is its unique landing-gear arrangement. It comprises three main wheels in tandem, a single nose wheel, and outriggers, all of which are retractable.

SO-5100—Airline, Transport Aircraft. It resembles the De Havilland "Comet" in many details. It is designated the "Champagne" and is powered by four Rolls-Royce Nene turbojet powerplants. Wing span is 84 feet, 7 inches. Over-all length is 61 feet. Total wing area is 910 square feet. Gross weight approximates 39,300 pounds, of which 10,000 pounds are engine fuel. Operational altitude is 33,000 feet. The range of the SO-5100 is 3,000 miles.

SO-1100—A Tip-jet-powered Helicopter. Designated the "Ariel," this aircraft is unique in that its tip-jet powerplants are supplied by a compressor, which, in turn, is coupled to a conventional air-cooled "Mathis G-8" piston engine. The eight-cylinder reciprocating engine develops 220 horsepower. The Ariel can cruise at 77 miles per hour. Its maximum speed approximates 100 miles per hour.

SO-4000—Experimental Jet-powered Bomber. Wing span is 58 feet, 7 inches. Over-all length is 64 feet, 10 inches. Weight (loaded) is 48,510 pounds. Wings are swept back at an angle of 31°. It is powered by two Hispano Nene turbojet powerplants with a total thrust output of 10,000 pounds. Its landing gear comprises a steerable nose wheel and two sets of main wheels, the independent legs of which retract into the wing panels. The SO-4000 carries a crew of two.

Arsenal VG 90—Single-place, Naval Fighter Airplane. A product of the Arsenal de l'Aéronautique, this aircraft has been developed from the earlier VG 70 design. The main wing member has a 25° sweep back and a span of 39 feet, 6 inches. Maximum speed approximates 600 miles per hour. Armament includes three 30-millimeter cannons, rockets, and bombs. A feature of this aircraft is its very wide landing-gear tread.

Nord-1601—Experimental, Twin-jet-powered Fighter Aircraft. Wing span is 40.7 feet. Total wing area is 325 square feet. Gross weight approximates 14,470 pounds. It is powered by two Rolls-Royce Derwent V turbojet powerplants, developing 3,500 pounds thrust each. Maximum speed is 620 miles per hour. Although the aircraft incorporates a tricycle landing gear, a small tail wheel is also provided.

It is a product of S.N.C.A.N. (Société Nationale de Construction Aéronautique du Nord), another of the French nationalized companies.

Nord-2200—Twin-jet-engined, Naval Fighter Aircraft. This is a modification of the Nord-1601. Wing span is 39 feet. Over-all length is 44 feet. Height from the ground to the top of the vertical fin is 11 feet, 8 inches. Gross weight approximates 17,650 pounds, while the empty weight is 10,650 pounds. It is powered by two Hispano-Suiza Nene turbojet powerplants. Performance figures include a maximum speed of 570 miles per hour at sea level and a cruising speed of 550 miles per hour at 15,000 feet. Rate of climb is 4,500 feet per minute. Service ceiling is 36,000 feet.

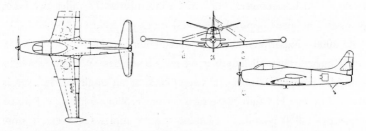

FIGURE 141. The French Bregeut 960 "Vultur" Naval Carrier Fighter-Bomber with Armstrong-Siddeley "Mamba" Propjet in Nose and Rolls-Royce Nene Turbojet in Rear of Fuselage.

Aerocenter NC-1080—Naval Fighter Airplane. This was developed from an earlier twin-jet-engined design designated as the NC-1071. The NC-1080 resembles the Vickers-Armstrong "Supermarine 510" in many details and is characterized mainly by similar, large, side-intake air ducts. It is further distinguished by its unusually large flaps and by oddly shaped fins, attached to the tail surfaces. This is a product of the Société Nationale de Constructions Aéronautique du Centre, still another of the French nationalized companies.

Grognard SE-2410—Twin-jet-engined Ground-attack Airplane. Another nationalized company, S.N.C.A.S.E. (Société Nationale de Constructions Aéronautique du Sud-Est), is responsible for the design and production of this airplane. Gross weight is 43,000 pounds. It is powered by two Hispano Rolls-Royce Nene turbojet powerplants, one superimposed on the other and utilizing a single air-intake duct. The drawbacks of this type of engine arrangement (susceptibility to local stalling and poor pressure recovery at high angles of attack) have been apparently eliminated. The wheels of the tricycle landing gear all retract into the fuselage, yielding an extremely narrow tread. In addition, a small tail wheel and bumper are provided. Unusual features of this airplane include low horizontal control surfaces which are located directly in the wing wake. A two-place version, the SE-2415, and an all-weather version, the SE-2421, are in development.

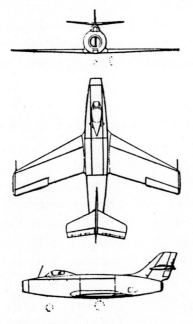

FIGURE 142. The French Mystère "MD 452" Fighter Aircraft.

Mystere MD 452—Jet-powered Fighter Aircraft. This design has indicated phenomenal performance. Its maximum speed is given as Mach 0.99, thus placing it definitely in the 650 mile per hour class. It was originally powered with a single Rolls-Royce Nene turbojet powerplant. Later models will have more power, employing either a Rolls-Royce Tay or a S.N.E.C.M.A. Atar powerplant. Wings are swept back at more than 35°. An outstanding feature of the airplane is its extreme maneuverability. This is attributed primarily to its relatively low wing loading of 45.06 pounds per square foot. By comparison, the wing loading of the F-86 "Sabrejet" is 60.22 pounds per square foot, while that of the Russian MIG-15 is 38.75 pounds per square foot.

The Mystère, like its immediate predecessor, the Dassault MD 450 "Ouragon" interceptor fighter, was developed and produced by a nonsubsidized manufacturer. Other aircraft in this category include the Bregeut 960 "Vultur," a naval strike fighter compositely powered by an Armstrong-Siddeley Mamba turbopropjet powerplant in the nose and a Rolls-Royce Nene turbojet in the rear of the fuselage, and the LeDuc 010, an experimental aircraft, powered by a single ramjet powerplant.

SWEDISH AIRCRAFT

Svenska Aeroplan AB SAAB-29—Single-place, Interceptor Fighter Airplane. This swept-wing aircraft is powered by a single De Havilland Ghost centrifugal-flow turbojet powerplant, developing 5,000 pounds thrust. It is planned to power subsequent designs with an improved version of the Swedish Skuten turbojet powerplant. This unit develops 3,200 pounds static thrust and is manufactured by Stal Svenska Turbinfarbriks A.B., Ljungstrom, Finspong. The SAAB airplane is characterized by its bulky fuselage. Performance figures include a maximum speed of 500 miles per hour.

ITALIAN AIRCRAFT

Fiat G.80—Two-place, Jet-powered Trainer. Wing span is 32 feet. Over-all length is 37 feet. Total wing area is 225 square feet. It is powered by a single De Havilland Goblin 4 turbojet powerplant, developing 3,500 pounds static sea-level thrust. Take-off gross weight approximates 11,000 pounds. Performance figures include a maximum speed of 547 miles per hour at the operational altitude of 29,550 feet.

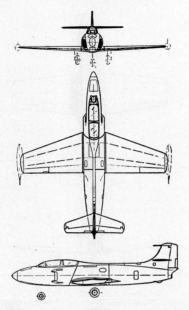

FIGURE 143. The Italian Fiat "G.80" Fighter.

Maximum range is 840 miles. The G.80 has been designed with inter-changeable nose sections. Installation of the various nose sections permits the use of the aircraft as a trainer, a single-seat fighter, a night fighter, or a photo reconnaissance aircraft. In many respects, the G.80 is similar to the Lockheed F-80 aircraft.

DUTCH AIRCRAFT

Fokker F.26—Transport Aircraft. Designated the "Phantom," it seats seventeen passengers. Wing span is 59 feet, 9 inches. Total wing area is 484 square feet. Gross weight is 25,360 pounds. Payload is estimated at 3,745 pounds. It is powered by two Rolls-Royce Nene turbojet powerplants, developing 5,000 pounds thrust each. Per-formance figures include a maximum speed of 500 miles per hour. Cruising speed of over 300 miles per hour on one engine at 30,000 feet is claimed possible. Range is 621 miles. Pressurization maintains 8,000-foot condition within the cabin when the aircraft is at its ceiling.

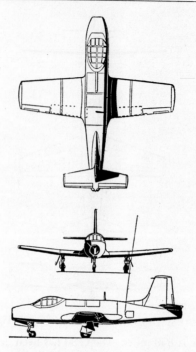

FIGURE 144. The Fokker "S.14" Jet Trainer (Powered by a Rolls-Royce "Derwent IX" Turbojet Powerplant).

Fokker S.14—Two-place Jet-powered Trainer Aircraft. The side-by-side seating arrangement is employed. The excellent performance of this aircraft is attributed primarily to its relatively low wing loading of 32.2 pounds per square foot. Comparable British and American converted jet trainers have wing loadings of 45 to 50 pounds per square foot. It is powered by a single Rolls-Royce Derwent IX turbojet powerplant. Maximum speed is in the region of 435 miles per hour.

ARGENTINE AIRCRAFT

Pulqui—Single-place, Jet-powered Fighter Airplane. It is designed and constructed by the Aero Techo Institute of the Argentine Air Force at Cordoba, Argentina. It is reportedly the creation of Kurt Tank, famed German aircraft designer. The aircraft is powered by a single

Rolls-Royce Derwent V turbojet powerplant, developing 3,600 pounds static thrust. Performance figures include a maximum speed over 500 miles per hour, a landing speed of 100 miles per hour, and a flight duration of approximately 1 hour.

Pulqui II—This is an improved version of the original design. The

FIGURE 145. The Argentine "Pulqui II" Fighter.

English translation of the aircraft name is "Arrow." The main wing members have a 35° sweep back. Shoulder mounted, the wing is of constant chord. The tricycle landing gear has an extremely narrow tread, as gaged by American and British standards. The airplane is fitted with a tee-tail, the horizontal stabilizer being mounted at the extreme upper end of the vertical fin. It is powered by a single Rolls-Royce Nene centrifugal-flow turbojet powerplant, developing 5,000 pounds thrust. A maximum speed of 1,000 kilometers per hour (621 miles per hour) has reportedly been attained. However, 450 miles per hour has been accepted as a more consistent figure.

RUSSIAN AIRCRAFT

Lavochkin Interceptor—Single-place, Interceptor Fighter Aircraft. Wing span is 35 feet, 9 inches. Over-all length is 39 feet, 6 inches. The wing is swept back at an angle of 45°. The vertical fin is swept back at 50°, and the horizontal tail plane, 40°. It is powered by a single Soviet M-012 axial-flow turbojet powerplant, developing 6,400 pounds static thrust. This powerplant is a redesignated German Junkers Jumo-012, and incorporates an eleven-stage axial compressor and

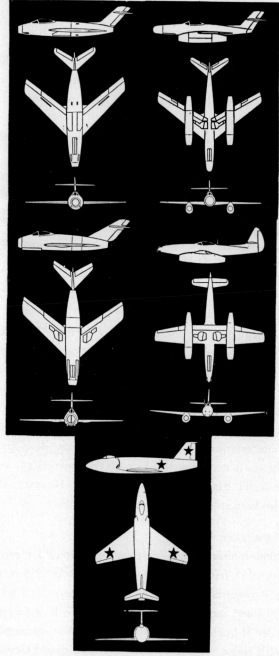

FIGURE 146. Russian Jet-powered Fighter Aircraft.

The Lavochkin
Single-jet
Interceptor

The Lavochkin Twin-jet
Night Fighter

The Mikoyan Jet
Fighter

The Lavochkin "LA-8"

The YAK "17" Fighter

a two-stage turbine. The Soviet M-018 turbojet powerplant is also used in Russian tactical aircraft. This engine is a redesignated German Junkers M-018, and is composed of a twelve-stage axial compressor, a twenty-four burner, annular combustion chamber, a three-stage turbine, and an adjustable propelling nozzle. The maximum speed of the airplane in question is 600 miles per hour. Built-in dive brakes are fitted to the wing in a position just forward of the flaps. The narrow-track landing gear retracts forward into the fuselage. This arrangement eliminates the necessity for wheel well bulges in the thin wing member.

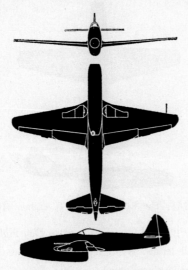

FIGURE 147. The Russian "YAK-15" Fighter Airplane.

Lavochkin Night Fighter—Single-place, Twin-jet-engined Fighter Aircraft. Wing span is 41 feet. Over-all length is 45 feet. The main wing is swept back at an angle of 35°. The vertical fin is of unusual height and is swept back 50°. The horizontal tail plane is swept back 40°. It is powered by German-designed, axial-flow turbojet powerplants. The underslung nacelles are of sufficient length to accommodate afterburner installations. Main landing gear legs retract inboard of the nacelles and are accommodated within the wing roots. Split flaps, divided into three sections, are located at the trailing edge of the main wing member. The nose section houses an A.I. radar scanner. Armament, consisting of various combinations of heavy-caliber cannon, is mounted on either side of the nose-wheel well. Maximum speed of the twin-jet aircraft approximates 650 miles per hour.

FIGURE 148. The Russian "MIG-9" Fighter Airplane.

Lavochkin Twin-jet Fighter—Single-place Day Fighter. Wing span is 42 feet. Over-all length is 38 feet. Neither the main wings nor the tail surfaces have sweep back in this design. The main wing members are tapered, both on the leading and trailing edges, outboard of the engine nacelles. The usual German-designed, axial-flow turbo-jet powerplants are mounted in jet pods beneath the main wings. Armament consists of four cannons, mounted in the nose section. Maximum speed is 600 miles per hour. The newest reported version of Lavochkin aircraft, designated the LA-17, has a long ventral fillet in the vertical stabilizer structure.

Mikoyan Interceptor—Single-place, Interceptor Fighter Aircraft. Wing span is 35 feet, 6 inches. Over-all length is 40 feet, 2 inches.

The main wing is swept back at an angle of 40°. The vertical stabilizer has a 60° sweep back and supports the 45° swept tail-plane member. The wing member is of extremely thin construction, as much so as to require bulged wheel wells for the retractable landing-gear legs. The airplane is powered by a single Rolls-Royce Nene centrifugal-flow turbojet powerplant. The large diameter of this powerplant dictates the requirement for the rather bulbous fuselage which characterizes the Mikoyan interceptor aircraft. An efficient, single-piece cockpit canopy is positioned far forward on the nose section to give 360° visibility to the pilot. Tubes, suitable for firing rockets or recoilless cannon projectiles, are located on either side of the nose section. The maximum speed of this aircraft is over 625 miles per hour.

FIGURE 149. The Russian "MIG-15" Fighter Airplane.

A very recent, improved version of the Mikoyan interceptor is the Mikoyan twin-jet-powered, ground-support fighter. Its wings are quite stubby and rounded at the tips. The air-intake ducts are elliptical. Tail-pipe members terminate at the wing root trailing edge. The swept-back tail plane is set high, although not in a tee-configuration. Armament comprises four cannons in the underside of the nose. The gun ports only are visible, since the gun muzzles do not protrude.

Yak-15—Single-place, Fighter Aircraft. This is a conventional airplane, with semielliptical wings and tail surfaces. Wing span is 33 feet. Over-all length is 30 feet. It is powered by a single, axial-flow turbojet powerplant that is typical of the German Junkers Jumo-004. The powerplant assembly is accommodated in an underslung housing which constitutes the underside of the forward fuselage structure. The resultant deep fuselage, with its large keel area, makes a dorsal fin fairing unnecessary. However, this installation necessitates a cockpit location aft of the trailing edge of the wing. Extremely poor pilot visibility results from this arrangement. From all indications, the Yak-15 aircraft is of composite wood and metal construction. Landing gear is of the tail-wheel type. Armament is mounted in the upper half of the nose section, just forward of the cockpit and consists of two Beresin 12.7-millimeter machine guns and one heavy bore ShVAK cannon. Maximum speed is 500 miles per hour.

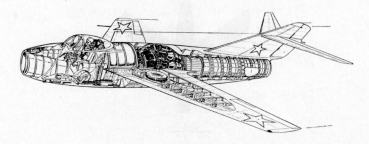

FIGURE 150. Cut-away Drawing of the Russian "MIG-15" Fighter Airplane.

Yak-17—Single-place, Fighter Aircraft. The wing member is swept back at an angle of 35°. It is square cut and has a medium-taper, straight-edged pattern. The tail surfaces are also square cut. The vertical stabilizer has no sweep back. The horizontal tail plane is swept back at an angle of 20° and is located high up on the vertical stabilizer. The single turbojet powerplant appears to be a Rolls-Royce

Nene, or a similar engine, and is mounted within the rear fuselage section. This arrangement, coupled with its midmounted wing member, gives the YAK-17 an aerodynamically clean appearance. In general, this airplane bears a marked resemblance to the British Supermarine line of jet-powered fighters. The cockpit canopy is of the bubble type and is set well forward, thus providing excellent pilot visibility. "Elephant ear" scoops, located well forward of the wing roots, furnish air to the turbojet powerplant. These large side intakes may constitute a barrier to supersonic flight speeds. Similar configurations have yielded very low values of efficiency in this respect. At all events, the maximum speed attained by the Yak-17 is 625 miles per hour.

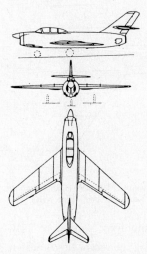

FIGURE 151. The Russian "MIG-15F" Two-place Night Fighter.

MIG-9—Single-place, Twin-jet-engined, Fighter Aircraft. Wing span is 42 feet. Over-all length is 38 feet. It is powered by two axial-flow turbojet powerplants. The original model was powered by Soviet redesignations of the German Junkers Jumo-003 turbojet. The two powerplants are mounted in parallel in the underside of the forward fuselage section. Divided nose intakes supply air to the two powerplants. The landing gear is of the tricycle type, the nose wheel retracting backward and upward between the previously mentioned, divided air-intake ducts. In general, the basic structure of the MIG-9 shows a close similarity to that of the German Messerschmitt ME-262A "Sturmvogel" (Storm Bird). Armament consists of two heavy-caliber machine guns and one heavy-bore cannon. The entire armament assembly is mounted in the nose section, the machine guns being placed one on each side and below the air intakes, and the cannon being in the center. Its maximum speed approximates 520 miles per hour.

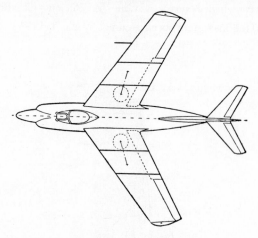

FIGURE 152. The Russian "MIG-19" (Identified by USAF Personnel in Korea as the "Flat MIG").

MIG-15—Newer, Improved Version of MIG-9. It has been observed over Korea during the recent hostilities. It is a swept-back mid-wing design, with a tricycle landing gear. Wing span is 32.5 feet. Over-all length is 32.8 feet. Gross weight approximates 12,500 pounds. Maximum speed is about 747 miles per hour. It is powered by a centrifugal-flow turbojet powerplant of the "Chelomey" type, based on the original Rolls-Royce Nene design. The nose air intake is divided to pass incoming air to either side of the cockpit. The main wing panels have a slightly tapered, low-aspect-ratio planform with a thin cross section adaptable to near-sonic speeds. It has a pilot-ejection seat. Distinctive features are the unusually large diameter of the nose air-intake duct and the manner in which the tail pipe is cut back beneath the vertical tail surfaces, ostensibly to reduce the thrust losses aft of the turbine.

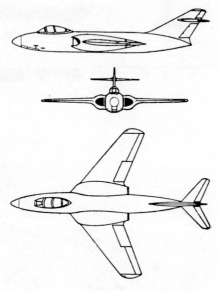

FIGURE 153. The Mikoyan Twin-jet Ground-support Fighter.

Tupolev TU-10—Jet-powered, Bombardment Aircraft. Wing span is 70 feet. Over-all length is 60 feet. It is powered by two M-004 turbojet powerplants. Maximum speed is 497 miles per hour. Maximum range is 2,000 miles. A crew of four is carried.

Ilyushin I1-16—Jet-powered, Bombardment Aircraft. Wing span is 87 feet. Over-all length is 70 feet. Gross weight approximates 80,-000 pounds. It is powered by four M-004 turbojet powerplants. Maximum speed is evaluated at 466 miles per hour. A crew of four is carried.

Tupolev-Gurevich Intercontinental Bomber—Long-range, Jet-powered, Bombardment Aircraft. This design is characterized by its

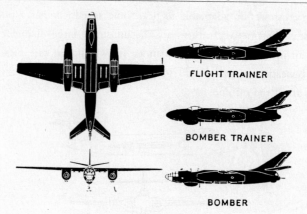

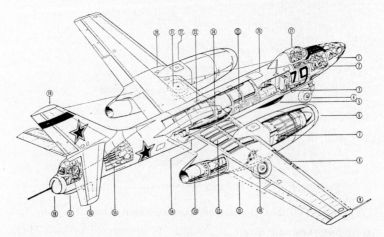

FIGURE 154. *The Russian Tupolev "TU-10" Bombardment Airplane:*
This aircraft can be employed as a flight trainer, a bomber trainer, and as a
tactical bombardment type. (1) bombsight; (2) bombardier/radar operator;
(3) 30 mm. cannon; (4) rearward-retracting nose wheel; (5) navigational-
search radar; (6) air intake; (7) M-018 axial jet powerplant of 7,700 pounds
thrust; (8) hot-air de-icing ducts; (9) pitot static tube; (10) semi-high-pres-
sure wheels; (11) "droop type" trailing edge flaps; (12) center-section fuel
cells; (13) afterburner; (14) highspeed bomb bay doors; (15) rear fuselage;
(16) 40°-sweep-back stabilizer; (17) tail bumper; (18) 20 or 23 mm. cannon
in electrically operated turret; (19) 40°-sweep-back fin and rudder; (20) outer
wing panels; (21) retracted main wheel; (22) powerplant nacelle; (23) main
fuel supply; (24) bomb bay; (25) vertical camera; (26) radio and radar equipment; (27) pilot's cockpit, slightly offset to port—all crew positions pressurized
and armored.

extremely thin wings and its circular fuselage. The main wings and horizontal tail surfaces have a 35° sweep back. Gross weight approximates 360,000 pounds. It is powered by six M-028 turbine powerplants, coupled to contra-rotating propellers. These powerplants represent Soviet adaptations of the German BMW-028 design, which, in turn, is an improved modification of the original BMW-018 turbine. The M-028 has a twelve-stage compressor, an annular combustion chamber, and a four-stage turbine which has been specially designed for high-altitude flying. It is rated at 6,900 equivalent shaft horsepower. For take-off and short speed bursts, a BMW-109-718 rocket motor is provided. This unit develops 6,600 pounds additional thrust. Turbo-prop powerplants have probably been selected in preference to turbo-jets, since, in general, they permit greater range and better fuel economy. Performance figures of the bomber include a maximum speed of about 500 miles per hour and a range of over 10,500 miles.

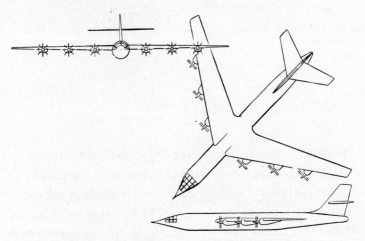

FIGURE 155. The Tupelov-Gurevich Intercontinental Bombardment Airplane.

CZECHOSLOVAKIAN AIRCRAFT

Avia AV-52—Single-seat, Ground-attacker, Fighter Airplane. Wing span is 37 feet, 7½ inches. Over-all length is 35 feet, 8 inches. Height from the ground to the top of the vertical fin is 11 feet, 7 inches. It has a square-cut, low-aspect-ratio wing and a long-stroke tricycle landing gear. It is powered by a single Jumo 004B-1 axial-flow turbojet powerplant, developing 3,080 to 3,960 pounds thrust. Performance figures include a maximum speed of 525 miles per hour, a cruising speed of 497 miles per hour, and a service ceiling of 41,338 feet. The range, under cruise conditions, is 466 miles. Armament includes two 30-millimeter, forward-firing cannons, mounted on either side of the fuselage nose. Two 992-pound bombs or RS.82 (Russian-style) rocket bombs can be transported by this airplane.

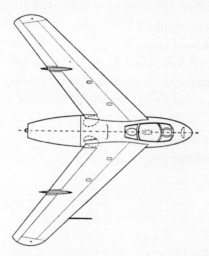

FIGURE 156. The Russian "EF-128" All-weather Fighter Airplane.

Nikol Suhag—This aircraft is a local version of the German jet-powered Messerschmitt ME-262, mentioned previously in the text.

Letov L-115—Two-place, All-weather, Fighter Airplane. Wing span is 49 feet, 2½ inches. Over-all length is 46 feet. It is powered by two Jumo 004B-1 turbojet powerplants, mounted in an unusual arrangement on the top of the fuselage. Performance figures include a maximum speed of 547 miles per hour, a cruising speed of 516 miles per hour, and a range of 795 miles. The range can be increased to 920 miles through the utilization of additional internal tankage.

This airplane, which is designated the "Delfin," is characterized by a thin, elliptical wing and side-by-side air-intake ducts.

SWISS AIRCRAFT

N-2010—Government-sponsored, Military, Jet-powered, Delta-wing Aircraft. Originally powered by a redesigned pure jet version of the British Armstrong-Siddeley "Mamba" turbopropjet powerplant. This powerplant unit was selected because of its small diameter. A newer, larger version of the aircraft, the N-2020, is contemplated to be powered with the British Armstrong-Siddeley "Sapphire" turbojet powerplant. Specifications of the N-2010 are as follows: wing span, 41.33 feet; over-all length, 41.29 feet; over-all height from the ground to the tip of the vertical stabilizer, 12.04 feet; gross weight, 19,030 pounds.

FIGURE 157. Chase XC-123A "Avitruc."

COMPARISON OF AXIAL-FLOW AND CENTRIFUGAL-FLOW TURBOJET POWERPLANT SPECIFICATIONS

Model: Westinghouse 19-B.

Type: Turbojet, continuous-cycle, single-stage turbine and six-stage, axial-flow compressor.

Compressor: One-piece, forged-aluminum-alloy rotor, with projecting hub at the front end, over which a steel sleeve is shrunk for front journal, and a flange at the rear end which is rigidly bolted to the flange on the front end of the turbine-rotor shaft; six rows of steel rotating compressor blades are held to the rotor by ball roots; all rows have the same tip diameter and tip speed; two-piece, cylindrical, cast-aluminum-alloy casing which holds five rows of stationary, steel compressor blades and three rows of aluminum-alloy straightening vanes; four mounting lugs at the rear flange.

Combustion Chamber: One cylindrical, stainless-steel combustion chamber which contains a double, annular burner basket; holes in the sides of the burner admit the air flow from the compressor; fuel is sprayed into the burner by twenty-four equally spaced nozzles located at the extreme front of the burner; the rear end of the combustion chamber is connected to the annular intake shroud of the turbine.

Turbine: Annular, stainless-steel casings with one row of vitallium-alloy nozzle vanes; one-piece, steel rotor disc with integral steel shaft; one row of thirty-two solid, Westinghouse K42B alloy blades attached to the rotor by ball roots.

Exhaust Nozzle: Welded, stainless-steel exhaust nozzle with stream-lined insulating lagging around the rear portion; the movable inner cone varies the outlet area and permits back-pressure control.

Fuel System: One Pesco 2P689-A positive-displacement fuel pump, capacity 0.611 cubic inch per revolution; twenty-four Monarch 10.5 gallon per hour F8OPLP spray nozzles; fuel pressure 500 to 501 per square inch (depending on the altitude); Purolator 303 fuel strainer.

Bearings and Lubrication: The compressor and turbine rotor are supported on three bearings: a ball thrust bearing in front of the combustion chamber and two sleeve-type bearings, one in front of the compressor and the other in front of the overhung turbine; one Nichols C 26C43032D64-A pressure and scavenge pump; one Purolator 303 oil filter; pressure fuel to bearings—8 pounds per square inch; hollow, cylindrical oil cooler attached to the engine at the inlet.

Starting System: Two Eclipse 1367 high-tension booster coils and two Champion 49 spark plugs, one on each side of the combustion chamber; Eclipse 41 direct-cranking electric starter with gear reducer.

Control: One Westinghouse 29J974 fuel-throttle valve; one Westinghouse 39J550 governor.

 Width: 25 25/32 inches

 Height: 25 11/16 inches

 Length: 89 27/32 inches

 Frontal Area: 3.8 square feet

 Weight: 809 pounds

 Weight/Maximum Thrust Ratio: 0.59

 Fuel Grade: 100 to 130 octane gasoline

 Oil Grade: AN-0-6

 Normal Fuel Consumption: 1.28 pounds per hour per pound thrust

 Normal Oil Consumption: 1 gallon per hour

 Rating (Military Static): 1,365 pounds thrust at 18,000 r.p.m. at sea level

 Rating (Normal Static): 1,175 pounds thrust at 17,000 r.p.m. at sea level

 Rating (Military Altitude): 525 pounds thrust at 18,000 r.p.m. at 30,000 feet at 500 miles per hour

 Rating (Normal Altitude): 465 pounds thrust at 17,000 r.p.m. at 30,000 feet at 500 miles per hour

 Compression Ratio (Maximum): 3:1

Centrifugal-flow Type

Model: General Electric I-40

Type: Turbojet, centrifugal-flow compressor

Impeller Diameter: 30 inches

Impeller-inlet Diameter: 18¼ inches

Impeller-hub Diameter: 8 inches

Diffuser-throat Area: 75 square inches

Fuel-nozzle Size: 40 gallons per hour at 100 pounds per square inch

Turbine-nozzle Area: 121.3 square inches

Turbine-pitch Diameter: 22 inches

Turbine-nozzle and Blade Height: 4 inches

Exhaust-pipe Diameter: 21 inches

Jet-nozzle Diameter: 19 inches

Maximum over-all Diameter: 48 inches

Over-all Length: 101½ inches

Average Weight: 1,820 pounds

Center of Gravity (aft of Trunnion): 2 inches

Thrust: 4,000 pounds

Fuel flow: 4,740 pounds per hours

Specific Fuel Consumption: 1,185 pounds per hour per pound thrust

Exhaust Temperature: 1,170° F.

Compression Ratio: 4.126

Compressor Discharge Temperature: 413° F.

Combustion-pressure Drop: 3.18 pounds per square inch

Turbine Inlet Temperature: 1,492° F.

Air Flow: 79 pounds per second

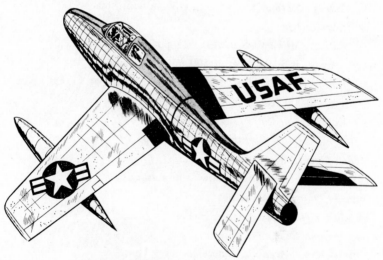

FIGURE 158. Republic "F-84F" Fighter Airplane.

All these average performance data were taken at 11,500 revolutions per minute, with standard inlet conditions of 14.7 pounds per square inch, 59° F., and 0 ram.

GENERAL JET-PROPULSION FORMULAS

Net Thrust = Mass × Change of Velocity

$$= \frac{(W_A + W_F)\, C - W_A V}{g} \quad \text{or}$$

$$\frac{W_A (C - V)}{g}$$

Thrust Power = Thrust × Flight Speed

$$= \frac{[(W_A + W_F)\, C - W_A V]\, V}{550g} \quad \text{or}$$

$$\frac{W_A (C - V)\, V}{550g}$$

Jet Power = Mass × Velocity Squared

$$= \frac{(W_A + W_F)\, C^2 - W_A V^2}{2g \times 550} \quad \text{or}$$

$$\frac{W_A (C^2 - V^2)}{2g \times 550}$$

Fuel Input Power = Fuel Flow × Fuel Heating Value

$$= W_F \times H_F \times \frac{J}{550}$$

Wake Efficiency = Thrust Power ÷ Jet Power

$$= 2 \left[\frac{(W_A + W_F)\, CV - W_A V^2}{(W_A + W_F)\, C^2 - W_A V^2} \right] \quad \text{or}$$

$$\frac{2V}{C + V}$$

Thermal Efficiency = Jet Power ÷ Fuel Input Power

$$= \frac{[(W_A + W_F)\, CV - W_A V^2]}{2 W_F H_F g J} \quad \text{or}$$

$$\frac{W_A (C^2 - V^2)}{2 W_F H_F g J}$$

Over-all Efficiency $=$ Thrust Power $\div$ Fuel Input Power

$$= \frac{[(W_A + W_F) \, CV - W_A V^2]}{W_F H_F g J} \quad \text{or}$$

$$\frac{W_A V \, (C - V)}{W_F H_F g J}$$

Symbols used in the preceding formulas:

$W_A =$ Free air used in propulsion (pounds/second)

$W_F =$ Fuel and mass transported in air frame (pounds/second)

$g \;\; =$ Acceleration of gravity (feet/second^2)

$C \;\; =$ Jet velocity relative to aircraft (feet/second^2)
  This quantity $=$ jet velocity relative
  to ground $+$ flight velocity

$V \;\; =$ Flight velocity (feet/second)

$H_F =$ Heating value of fuel; (British thermal units/pound)
  use lower value

$J \;\; =$ Mechanical equivalent of heat

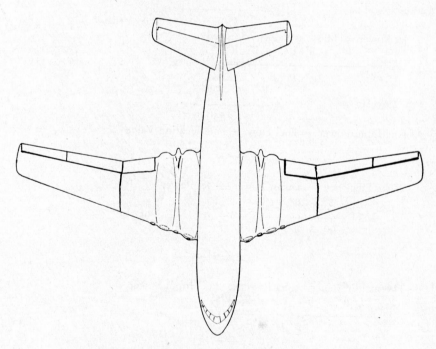

FIGURE 159. British De Havilland "Comet" Jet-Powered
Transport Airplane.

SAFETY PRECAUTIONS

While turbojet-powered aircraft are parked on the ground, it is advisable to stay at least 25 feet away from the powerplant intake ducts. In general, the suction developed is not sufficiently powerful to be considered dangerous, even at slightly smaller distances. However, possible loss of balance and inadvertent approach to areas within the danger zone must be considered. Always remember that ground personnel have actually been drawn into jet intake scoops with resultant injury and even death. Loose caps, flying glasses, and tools have been lost in this manner. Resulting engine damage must also be considered.

The heat blast of the turbojet powerplant, emanating from the tail pipe, is perceptible at distances up to 75 feet. A representative turbojet blast involves velocities of the order of 80 miles per hour and temperatures up to 150° F. These figures are based on full take-off power. There are slight variations for different types of turbojet powerplants. Within a distance of 30 feet from the tail-pipe opening, the blast velocity is approximately 180 miles per hour, and the temperature is of the order of 300° F. An afterburner will yield even higher tem-

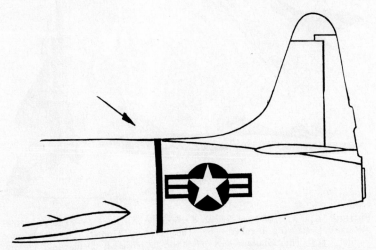

FIGURE 160. Two-inch Stripe Indicating the Position of the Turbine Wheel.

peratures. It is, therefore, obvious that approaching within these danger-zone limits can result only in disaster.

Aircraft powered by turbojet powerplants must not be approached too closely while flying, particularly from the rear. Internal tail-pipe temperatures as high as 800° F. are indicated during flight, with power settings in the region of 70% r.p.m. This figure indicates the condition of the wake area behind an air-borne jet aircraft.

The two-inch stripe, painted around the entire periphery of the rear section of the fuselage housing the turbojet powerplant, marks the position of the turbine wheel. This is a distinct danger area when the powerplant is being run up. Should the turbine wheel fail for any reason, the fragments would fly through the fuselage, with resultant injury to anyone standing in line with the stripe. This marking is illustrated in figure 160.

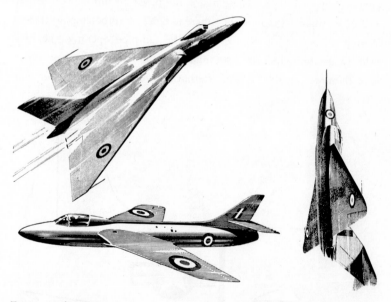

FIGURE 161. Trio of New British Tactical Jet Aircraft: (a) The Avro 698 "Vulcan" Delta-wing Bomber; (b) The Hawker "Hunter" Day Interceptor Fighter; (c) The Gloster "GA/5" Twin-Jet-powered, Delta-wing Fighter, the "Javelin."

Manufacturer and Address	Mfr's Designation	Military	Type	Comp. stages	Turb. stages	Static thrust @ S.L. (lb.)	At rpm	Rated thrust (lb.), S.L.	At rpm	Shaft hp.	At rpm	Equivalent shp. @ S.L.	At rpm	Propeller reduction gear ratio	Specific fuel consumption	Compressor air mass flow (lb./sec.)	Corresponding pressure ratio	Max. length (in.)	Max. dia. (in.)	Dry weight (lb.)	Accessories (lb.)	Total weight (lb.)	Make starter	Type starter	Approving agency	Time (hr.)	Engine status	Planes Using
Allison division General Motors Corp. Indianapolis, Ind.	400-D12	J33-A-33	CPJ	11	1	4600[1]	11,750	3900	11,250						1.16	89	4.4:1	213	49.31	1786	679[2]	2465	GE	Elec.	USAF	500	IP	F-94A, T-33, TO-2
	400-C13	J33-A-35	CPJ	11	1	4600[3]	11,750	3900	11,250						1.44	89	4.4:1	107	50.5	1702	93[2]	1795	GE	Elec.	USAF	500	IP	T-33, TO-2
	450-D10	J35-A-21	AFJ	11	1	5100	7900	4400	7500						1.21	85	4.9:1	195	37	2149	486[3]	2635	GE	Elec.	USAF	300	IP	F-89
	501-A4	T38-A	AFP	19	4						14,300	2763		11:1	1.58[6]			149.5	40			1540	AR	Air			X	Convair Turboliner
	500-A6	T40-A-6	AFP	19[a]	4[a]						14,300			11:1	1.64			185	45			2575	AR	Air			X	XA2D-1, XP5Y-1
Fredric Flader, Inc. 883 Division St. No. Tonawanda, N. Y.	124	J55-PF-1	AFJ			770	28,200	700	26,800									79	45	300		300	Br				X	
General Electric Co. Aircraft Gas Turbine div. 920 Western Ave. Lynn, Mass.	TG-190-C	J47-GE-11*	AFJ	12	1	5200[11]	7850	4320*	7370*						1*	90*	5.1*	144	36.75			2500[4]	GE	Elec.			IP	
	TG-190-D	J47-GE-17	AFJ	12	1	5200												225*	36.75				GE	Elec.			IP	
	TG-190-E	J47-GE-23	AFJ	12	1	5200												144	36.75			2500[4]	GE	Elec.			X	
Pratt & Whitney Aircraft div. United Aircraft Corp. East Hartford, Conn.	JT-6B	J42	CPJ			5750[10]												103.2	49.5			1723			USN	300	IP	F9F-2
	JT-7	J48	CPJ			6250[11]		4000										103.2	50			2000					IP	F-94C, F9F-5
		J57	AFJ	11	3	10,000*									.62												X	
	PT-2	T34	AFP	13								5700		11:1	1.09												OP	B-17G
Westinghouse Electric Corp. Aviation Gas Turbine div. Phila., Pa.	24C4B	J34-WE-22	AFJ	11	2	3000[11]	12,500	2290									7:1	154	33			2550	West.	Elec.			IP	XA3D-1, XF4D-1
	40E	J40	AFJ			8000[11,12]												120	24			1200					X	XF10F-1, XF3H-1
	24C-10	J46	AFJ			6000[11]																					X	
Wright Aeronautical Corp. Division of Curtiss-Wright Corp. Wood-Ridge, N. J.	YJ65-W-1	Typhoon	AFJ	13	2	7220												133.85	37.3			2580					IP	
	Typhoon		AFP	18	2					1410	14,500	1570	14,500	10.37:1	.916			79.83	52.8			2000					X	
	Typhoon		AFP	10	2					3820	15,000	3140	15,000	10.37:1	.669							3485					X	
	Typhoon		AFP	14	2					4100	8000	1550	8000	7.4:1	.765			122.77	54.5								X	

* — Approximate.
AFJ — axial-flow turbojet.
AFP — axial-flow turboprop.
CFJ — centrifugal-flow turbojet.
CFP — centrifugal-flow turboprop.

IP — in production.
X — experimental.
OP — out of production.
GE — General Electric.
AR — AiResearch.
Br — Breeze.

[1] 2.5 with afterburner.
[2] Includes components weights.
[3] 5400 lb. with water/alcohol injection.
[4] Takeoff with water/alcohol; 32.6 1.5 gpm.
[5] Starter-generator.
[6] Based on equivalent ship.
[7] Maximum width.
[8] Each engine.
[9] Also for -13, -15 and -19.
[10] Using water/alcohol injection.
[11] More than 8000 lb. with afterburner.
[12] 12,500 lb. with afterburner.

United States Aircraft Gas-turbine Engines

Manufacturer & Address	Designation	Type	Compressor stages	Turbine stages	Static thrust @ S.L. (lb.)	At rpm.	Rated thrust (lb.)	At rpm.	Shaft hp.	At rpm.	Equivalent shp. @ S.L.	At rpm.	Max. cont. cruising eshp.	At rpm.	At altitude (ft., & mph)	Max. residual thrust (lb.)	Propeller reduction gear ratio	Fuel flow (gph.)	Specific fuel consumption (lb./hr./shp. or lb./hr./thrust)	Compressor air mass flow @ max. rpm. @ S.L. static, (lb./sec.)	Corresponding pressure ratio	Turbine inlet (deg. C)	Maximum tailpipe (deg. C)	Maximum length (in.)	Maximum dia. (in.)	Dry weight (lb.)	Total weight (lb.)	Make starter supplied with engine	Type starter supplied with engine	Engine time allowed between overhauls (hr.)	Engine status
AUSTRALIA Commonwealth Aircraft Corp. Pty. Ltd., Fisherman's Bend, Pt. Melbourne	Nene 2VH	CFJ	1	1	5000	12,500	4000	11,800											1.09	88	4.4:1	745		96.8	49.3	1600		Rotax		200	IP
CANADA A. V. Roe Canada Ltd., Malton, Ont.	Orenda	AFJ	11		7000+		4000																135	42						IP
ENGLAND Armstrong Siddeley Motors Ltd., Parkside, Coventry	Adder I[1]	AFJ	10		1050		15,000												.916				560					Elec.		
	Mamba ASM3	AFP	10						1320	15,000	1476	15,000	1270	14,500	15,000 SL/300	405	.08945[3]	140	.90	17.6	5:1	867	590	42.30	28	550		Rotax	Elec.		
	Double Mamba ASMD1	AFP	10						2640	15,000	2951	15,000	2520	14,500	15,000 SL/300	810	.0964	135	.73	18	5:1	877	594	57.83	29	780		ASM*	Air		
	Python 1	AFP	14						3670	8000	4112	8000	3260	7600	7600 SL/300	1150	.135	355	.69	17.6	5:1	877	594	79.83	52.87	2000		ASM*	Air		
	Sapphire ASSa3	AFJ	12[12]	2	7220		15,000													52.5	7:1		590*	96.77	54	3350		ASM*	Air	SC	
	Viper AV2[0]	AFJ			1575																				2500		ASM	Air	IP	
Bristol Aeroplane Co., Ltd., Filton House, Bristol	Proteus 2	AFP	12[11]	3					3200	10,000	3510	10,000	1025	9500	35,000		.084	272	.69	45		720		140.15	35.25	3050		BTH, R	Elec.		X
	Coupled Proteus	AFP	12[11]	3					6400	10,000	7020	10,000	2050	9500	35,000		.088	544	.69	90				113.35	38.5	8106		BTH, R	Elec.		X
	Theseus 502	AFP	8[11]	3					2220	8200	2500	8200	1170	7800	20,000	145	.094	125	.773	30		690		167.3	80.4[7]	2205		BTH, R	Elec.		X
de Havilland Engine Co., Ltd., Stonegrove, Edgware, Middlesex	Ghost 50	CFJ	1	1	5000	10,250	4300	9750											1.19	87	4.35:1	735	690	82.6	54	2170		BTH, R	Elec.	350	IP
	Goblin 35	CFJ	1	1	3500	10,750	2950	10,250											1.08	63	3.6	800	690	70	53	1610		Rotax	Elec.	250	IP
Rolls-Royce Ltd., Derby	Avon R.A. 3[‡]	AFJ		1	7600[?]	14,700	3090	14,100														720		57	49.9	2208		Rotax	Elec.		IP
	Derwent 5 & 8	CFJ	1	1	3600	12,500	4000	11,800											1.05	64.5	4.51	860	650	126	41.5	1654		Rotax			IP
	Dart 504	CFP	2	1					1400	14,500	1400	14,500	1120	13,800	SL	365	.106	525	1.05[5]	83.1		540		95.2	38.5	929					IP
	Nene 3	CFJ	1		5100		11,800									145*			1.06	89.5	4.51	870	400	96.8	49.5	1024					IP
FRANCE Societe Nationale d'Etude et de Construction de Moteur d'Aviation, 150 Boulevard Haussmann, Paris 13	ATAR 101B	AFJ	7	1	4840	8050	2070		1055	14,000	1450	14,000				190			1.1		4.2:1	750	580	111.96	34.8	1870	1621[?]	ATAR, R.P. Elec.			IP
	TB 1000	AFP	9	2											15,400				.66					108	27	1080	1430				IP
Societe de Construction et d'Equipments Mechaniques pour l'Aviation, 60 Rue de Londres, Paris 8e	TGA I bis	AFP	15	4					1600		6350						5.77		1.03		3.8:1	600	400	120	36[7]	4360					
	TGAR 1008	AFJ	8	1	4650	6600															3.8:1	800	640	110	36[7]	2750					
	TR 1008	AFJ	8	5	5290	6600																850	670	84	39	2320					
Turbomeca, Bordes	Pimene	CFJ	1	1	220	180													1.05					31.5	15.75	120					

*Approximate.
AFJ — Axial flow turbojet.
AFP — Axial flow turboprop.
CFJ — Centrifugal flow turbojet.
CFP — Centrifugal flow turboprop.
Elec. — Electric.

Eshp.— Equivalent shaft horsepower.
IP — In production.
P — ATAR 2-stroke 25-hp. gas engine.
R — Rotax.
SC — Special category.
X — Experimental.

[1] Includes starter, pumps, etc.
[2] Turbojet version of Mamba.
[3] Standard ratios: .0845:1; .1138:1; .0972:1.
[4] Or Rotax electric.
[5] Lb./hr./eshp.
[6] Five-minute limit.
[7] Maximum width.

[8] Or BTH or Rotax turbo.
[9] With tailpipe.
[10] Expendable turbojet for missiles.
[11] Plus 1 centrifugal stage.
[12] The experimental R.A.2 Avon's official rating is 6000 lb. thrust.
[13] Includes starter.

Foreign Aircraft Gas-turbine Engines

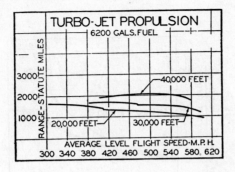

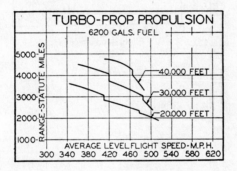

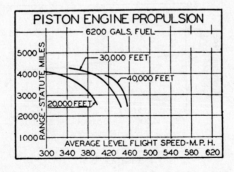

Speed vs Range Curves for Three Forms of Aircraft Propulsion

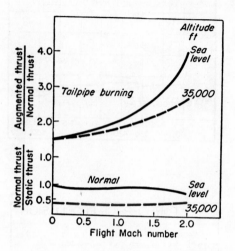

FIGURE A

Effect of Flight Conditions on Thrust

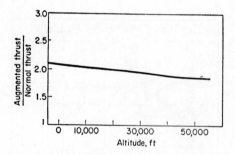

FIGURE B

Variation of Augmented Thrust with Altitude

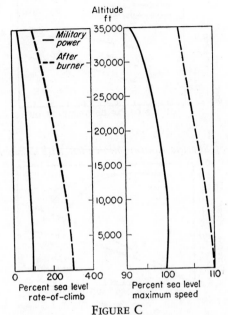

FIGURE C

Effect of Afterburner Power on Thrust

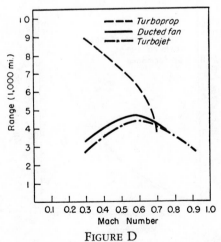

FIGURE D

Variation of Range with Mach Number

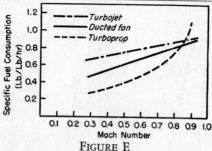

FIGURE E

Variation of Specific Consumption Fuel with Mach Number

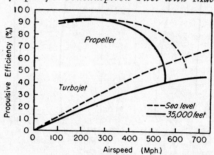

Figure F

Relationship of Propulsive Efficiency and Air Speed

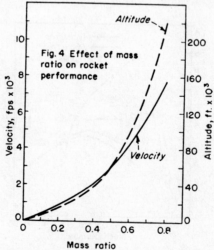

Effect of Mass Ratio (Weight of Propellant/Gross Weight)
on Rocket Velocity

GLOSSARY OF TERMS

AERORESONATOR. A duct-type jet powerplant, in which the atmospheric air for combustion is introduced by high forward velocity instead of a power-driven compressor. The periodic pulsing of the explosions within the duct determines the actuating cycle of the powerplant.

AFTERBURNING. Spraying fuel into the tail-pipe extension of a turbojet powerplant and burning it there. This increases the mass and velocity of the gases already in the turbojet exhaust stream. Actually, an afterburner is an attached ramjet powerplant.

AIR ADAPTER. The connecting element between the compressor outlet and the combustion chamber in a centrifugal-flow turbojet powerplant. The air adapter carries the fuel nozzle, the dome or end cap of the combustion chamber, and the spark plug, where provided.

AIR-FREE POWERPLANT. Any form of heat engine which uses oxygen from the atmosphere for combustion.

ATHOYD. Abbreviation of "Aero Thermo Dynamic Duct." A simple jet powerplant, consisting essentially of an open duct and having no moving parts. It is also called ramjet.

AXIAL-FLOW PRINCIPLE. Passing a straight flow of air through multiple compressor blades disposed about a central axis, as distinguished from the whirling pattern of the large-diameter centrifugal impeller.

BAROMETRIC FUEL CONTROL. An aneroid device which maintains a constant power output in jet powerplants in spite of variations in altitude.

BIPROPELLANT FUEL. A rocketjet fuel, consisting of two basic ingredients—one of them oxygen. These are injected into the combustion chamber separately, combustion occurring automatically on their contact.

BRAKE THERMAL EFFICIENCY. The ratio of the actual power output of a powerplant to the input, this last entity being expressed in terms of specific fuel consumption in pounds per brake horsepower per hour.

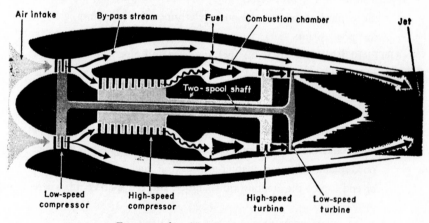

FIGURE 162. The Bypass Turbine Engine.

BYPASS TURBINE ENGINE. A turbine powerplant incorporating a method of diverting a portion of the intake air around the compressor and turbine components so as to discharge directly into the tailpipe jet stream. This arrangement slows down the jet exit velocity and minimizes "slip" (deviation between jet exit velocity and aircraft forward velocity). In addition, a distinct cooling effect is imparted to the discharge gases when the colder bypassed air is integrated with them. The bypass engine is similar to the ducted fan powerplant, the main difference being in the amount of air mass handled. An example of the bypass unit is the Rolls-Royce "Conway" turbojet powerplant.

CATALYST. A chemical agent that changes the rate of (usually accelerates) a chemical reaction, but is recovered unchanged at the end of the reaction. In rocketjet powerplants, potassium permanganate is used as a catalyst in order to accelerate combustion of the fuel ingredients.

CENTRIFUGAL-FLOW PRINCIPLE. The method of imparting a whirling pattern to air by the impeller blades of a centrifugal compressor, as contrasted with the straight-through pattern of axial flow.

CHEMICALLY FUELED ROCKET. A rocketjet using liquid oxygen with some form of hydrocarbon fuel, such as gasoline or alcohol.

CLAMSHELL. Variable-area exhaust nozzle of a turbojet powerplant. So called because of the resemblance of its lips to those of a clamshell-type excavator bucket.

CLOSED-CIRCUIT LUBRICATION SYSTEM. At the high altitudes at which turbojet powerplants operate, the barometric pressure drops to such a low level that the oil-pressure pump cannot be completely filled. Also, aeration of the lubricating oil becomes excessive at high altitudes. Due to this combined effect, there is hardly any oil delivery at altitudes above 50,000 feet. Lubrication ceilings can be raised by the installation of a pressurized tank, a booster pump, or a closed lubrication system. The last device is shown in figure 63. The scavenge pump operates as a booster to the pressure pump. The requirement for an extra booster pump is thus eliminated.

COLD ROCKET UNIT. A rocketjet powerplant operated at a comparatively low temperature. It is generally driven by a hydrogen-peroxide-base fuel, to which a relatively small amount of methyl alcohol is added. Combustion is brought about by a suitable catalyst.

COLD WORKING OF STEEL. The rolling and forging of steel alloys at relatively low finishing temperatures in order to increase their strength and hardness.

COMBUSTION. The actual ignition and burning of the ingredients of a fuel in combination with an adequate amount of air.

COMPOUND POWERPLANT. A combination of powerplants consisting of a reciprocating engine and a gas turbine. The exhaust gases of the reciprocating engine are employed to operate the gas turbine.

COMPRESSIBILITY. The point at which a moving object begins to create waves in the fluid medium through which it is passing.

CONSTANT-PRESSURE-CYCLE. The operating cycle of a gas turbine, in which combustion occurs at constant pressure within open passages between an air compressor and the turbine.

CONSTANT-VOLUME-CYCLE. The operating cycle of a gas turbine, in which combustion occurs at constant volume within a confined chamber; valves bring the combustion gases into direct contact with the turbine rotor blades.

CONTRA-ROTATING PROPELLERS. Dual propellers, rotating in opposite directions through reduction gearing; the torque forces, set up by each of the propeller units, tend to neutralize each other.

CREEP. The tendency of steel alloys to expand at sustained high temperature and rotation, which is detrimental for turbine rotor blades which are designed to clear casing structures with close tolerances.

CYCLE OF OPERATION. The complete sequence of steps in a heat engine, including the intake and compression of air, combustion, expansion, and the elimination of the waste combustion gases.

DIFFUSER. The forward extremity of an aeroresonator powerplant, designed with increasing cross section to permit inducted atmospheric air to expand slightly.

DIFFUSER VANES. A system of guide vanes through which heated combustion gases are directed to the turbine rotor blades of a turbojet powerplant.

DRY-FUELED ROCKET. A rocketjet utilizing a slow-burning powder as fuel, the oxygen required for complete combustion being incorporated within the powder.

EXHAUST CONE. The rear section of a turbojet powerplant, through which the heated combustion gases are ejected after passage through the turbine rotor blades.

EYELIDS. Partial enclosures at the exhaust end of an afterburner unit; they are opened by hydraulic pressure to give greater exhaust area; they are closed again to reduce the exhaust area as the afterburner is shut down.

FLAME HOLDER. A turbulence-producing grid device inserted in the high-velocity gas stream of a ramjet powerplant or an afterburner unit; its function is to decelerate the air flow so that continuous combustion can be maintained.

FLAME-OUT. Sudden stoppage of an aircraft turbojet powerplant. This may occur for a variety of reasons: fuel failure, ignition failure, clogging of the air-intake scoop, malfunctioning of turbine or compressor structural components, and even certain attitudes of the aircraft caused by prolonged and excessive forward control pressures; in fact, anything that might cause loss of combustion.

FLAME TUBE. Combustion chamber liner (British).

FLAP VALVE. An automatic air-intake valve employed on aero-resonator powerplants. The valve comprises a multiple grid, or grille, and resembles a series of unbalanced shutters.

GAS-STREAM UNIT. Central-turbine powerplant for actuating a jet-propelled helicopter aircraft.

GAS TURBINE. A form of heat engine comprising a rotor, fitted with suitable blading, mounted on a central shaft; heated combustion gases are directed against the turbine blades, imparting rotation to them; an air compressor of adequate capacity, mounted on the central shaft and driven by the turbine unit, and a combustion chamber complete the powerplant assembly.

HEAT EXCHANGER. A device, inserted between the compressor and the turbine unit, which functions in heating the entering air, after compression, to the temperature of the exhaust gases; its purpose is to recover a fraction of the heat energy dissipated in the turbine exhaust gases.

HOLZWARTH EXPLOSION TURBINE. A gas-turbine powerplant of intermittent action, operating on the constant-volume cycle.

HOT ROCKET UNIT. A rocketjet in which the over-all operating efficiency is improved by increasing combustion temperature by the utilization of highly concentrated fuel.

HOT WORKING OF STEEL. The initial upsetting of a definite length of billet or bloom at high temperature, prior to performing the actual forging procedure.

IMPELLER, COMPRESSOR. The rotating member of a compressor, comprising the compressor blades; it can be single-sided or double-sided.

IMPULSE TURBINE. A simple turbine unit in which expansion of the heated gases occurs within stationary nozzles or guide-vane passages, as distinguished from the reaction-type turbine.

INDICATOR DIAGRAM. The curve, plotted with values of pressure as ordinates and with values of volume as abscissae, for the entire working cycle of an internal-combustion powerplant; in the case of the gas turbine, the abscissae represent the volume of 1 pound of the working fluid at various stages of the cycle; the diagram area, bounded by the completed curve, then represents the potential energy of 1 pound of the working fluid.

INTERCOOLER. A device, inserted between the progressive stages of compression, which lowers the temperature of the air prior to reentering the compressor; its purpose is to reduce the power requirements of the compressor drive.

JATO. The abbreviation for jet-assisted take-off; auxiliary rocket power, furnishing supplemental thrust for the take-off of heavily loaded aircraft.

JET DISCHARGE. The mass of heated gases discharged per second, which, when multiplied by the jet velocity of the aircraft, determines the thrust force for a specified condition.

JET PROPULSION. A method by which an impelling force imparts forward motion to an aircraft due to the reactive thrust generated by the rearward-directed discharge of high-pressure, high-temperature combustion gases; the internal reactive force is impressed on the structure of the jet powerplant, thus producing forward motion.

KINETIC ENERGY. Any form of energy which consists in, or depends on, motion, as distinguished from potential energy.

LIQUID-FUELED ROCKETS. See Chemically Fueled Rockets.

LIQUID INJECTION. The spraying of water, usually mixed with methanol, into the inlet duct of a turbojet powerplant; evaporation of the liquid tends to lower the temperature of the incoming air to be compressed; this arrangement permits the burning of more fuel and thus an increase of the mass flow.

MACH NUMBER. A basic reference designating the velocity characteristics of an aircraft; a Mach number of 0.5, e.g., indicates a performance of 50 percent of the velocity of sound

$$\text{Mach number} = M = v/a, \text{ where } v = \text{local}$$

velocity and $a =$ local velocity of sound.

SPEED M.P.H	600	700	800	900	1000	2000	5000	10000	15000	20000	30000
MACH NUMBER AT SEA LEVEL	.79	.92	1.05	1.18	1.31	2.63	6.57	13.14	19.72	26.30	39.40

MECHANICAL EFFICIENCY. The ratio of the actually observed power output of an internal-combustion powerplant to its indicated power output; the difference between the two represents frictional and pumping losses.

MICROCAST PROCESS. Precision casting used for making aircraft turbojet-engine power blading. Castings of intricate design can be made by this process from high-melting-point alloys which assures surface smoothness and dimensional uniformity. Micro-castings need little or no machining. Machine tools are thus freed for other applications.

MONOPROPELLANT FUEL. A rocketjet fuel containing the oxidizing agent in stable form at normal temperatures; at a certain temperature increase, the oxygen of the oxidizing agent is released to cause spontaneous combustion of the fuel.

MOUTH ORGAN. The sobriquet given the pulsejet powerplant, particularly the grid-flap-valve type of the German V-1 aircraft.

NOSE BLOWING. Artificial respiration for starting turbojet-powered military aircraft in cold weather. The exhaust blast of a forward-positioned, jet-powered aircraft, accelerated to full power (100% r.p.m.), is made to windmill the powerplant of an idle aircraft located directly to the rear. Speeds higher than normal firing speeds must be attained in order to effect a normal start. When executing this maneuver, external power units and battery systems can be dispensed with. Sufficient distance must be provided to protect the pilot, airframe, and powerplant from the excessive heat and blast effects of the high-temperature exhaust gases. Pilots, when starting, must wear oxygen masks.

OPEN CYCLE. The simple operating cycle of the aircraft internal-combustion turbine, involving the three elements: compressor, combustor, and turbine.

POWDER METALLURGY. A special branch of metallurgy for the manufacture of parts from metal powders by pressing and heat treatment. It is used for making turbine blades.

PROPELLER EFFICIENCY. The ratio of the thrust delivered by a propeller to the power input to the propeller.

PROPJET POWERPLANT. An assembly of a gas turbine, rotating a conventional-type aircraft propeller on the forward end of its central power shaft and supplementing its thrust by the rearward-directed, jetted exhaust gases.

PULSEJET POWERPLANT. A compressorless aeroduct powerplant, the actuating cycle of which involves a periodic pulsing of the explosions occurring within its open conduit.

RAM. Impact air inlet pressure. Essential to efficient performance of the jet powerplant. There is a 2 percent reduction in thrust for each 1 percent loss in ram pressure. In general, a one-pound pressure drop would cause a decrease of approximately 15 percent in thrust.

RAMJET POWERPLANT. The simplest form of aeroduct powerplant, containing no moving parts of any kind.

RATTLERS. Mechanical vibrators installed on the instrument panels of jet-powered aircraft to insure functioning of all instruments.

REACTION TURBINE. A turbine powerplant, incorporating alternate sets of stationary and rotating blades; the heated combustion gases expand either partially or completely within the moving blades. See also Impulse Turbine.

REACTIVE PROPULSION. See Jet Propulsion.

RECIPROCATING ENGINE. The conventional form of powerplant, in which the reciprocating motion of the pistons is translated into rotary motion at the crankshaft.

REGENERATOR. See Heat Exchanger.

ROCKETJET POWERPLANT. A jet powerplant which transports the oxygen content required for complete combustion of its fuel.

ROTOR ASSEMBLY. Turbine powerplant components, comprising the central power shaft, compressor impeller, and turbine rotor.

ROSSLYN METAL. A "sandwich" metal, consisting of a copper core between stainless-steel coverings, joined by diffusion bonding. The steel imparts strength. The copper contributes good heat conductivity, the favorable heat dissipation relieving high stresses.

This metal is admirably suited for such applications as turbojet-powerplant combustor liners, tail pipes, and turbine buckets.

SOLID LUBRICATION. The use of viscous oil as a jet-engine lubricant instead of an air-oil spray. The newer models of Allison J-35 powerplants pioneered this system. Design engineers hesitated to use solid lubricants previously for fear they would tend to impose excessive bearing loads.

SONIC SPEED. The velocity of sound, which approximates 764 miles per hour at sea level and 664 miles per hour at an altitude of 40,-000 feet above sea level.

SPOOLING. An arrangement of compression stages for high compressor efficiency; in practice, a low-stage compressor precedes a high-stage unit which is connected to the first turbine wheel; the second turbine wheel is, in turn, connected to the low-stage compressor by hollow shafting. The "two spool," or split, compressor permits the use of compression ratios up to 12.0:1, with greatly increased flexibility and combustion efficiency over the single unit. Examples are the Pratt and Whitney "J-57," and the British Bristol "Olympus" turbojet powerplants.

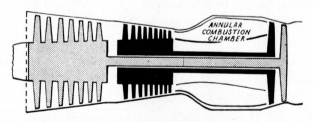

FIGURE 163. Two-spool Turbojet, Indicating its Separate Turbines and Compressors.

STANDARD DAY. Set of standard conditions established by the National Advisory Committee for Aeronautics (NACA) to guarantee thrust output, specific fuel consumption, and tail-pipe temperature in jet-aircraft powerplants. These are: 29.92 inches mercury barometric pressure; 0.076 pounds per cubic foot air density; and 0.0 water-vapor pressure. Deviation from these values is definitely noticeable, e.g., 1 inch water-vapor pressure affects thrust output by 75 pounds.

SUPERSONIC PROPELLER. A projected design of aircraft propeller contemplated for use with aircraft operating at speeds higher than that of sound.

TAIL CONE. See Exhaust Cone.

TAILPIPE TEMPERATURE INDICATOR. A thermocouple unit which indicates the temperature of the exhaust gases in jet power-plants; this indication is balanced against turbine rotor revolutions per minute in much the same manner as manifold pressure is balanced against engine revolutions per minute in the recipro-cating powerplant.

THERMAL BARRIER. The problem presented by the compounded effects of frictional, or aerodynamic, heating and the radiation from the jet powerplant. An aircraft flying at 1,000 miles per hour at sea level attains temperatures as high as 150° F by the passage of air across its external surfaces. To this is added 110° F for the Air Force standard dry, hot day, as well as part of the 2,000° F attending the tailpipe discharge gases. Solution entails the use of structural materials that retain strength under high temperatures

FIGURE 164. Jet Tail Pipe Thermometer.

and refrigeration systems that require as much as 2,600 equivalent horsepower from the jet power plant for their drive.

THERMOCOUPLE. Temperature indicator, which, in aircraft power-plants, incorporates an iron and a constantan lead, whose difference of potential is indicated on the temperature scale of the gage located in the cockpit.

THERMODYNAMIC EFFICIENCY. The ratio of the heat transformed into useful work to the heating value of the fuel utilized in a powerplant.

THIRD LAW OF MOTION. Law of physics, proposed by Sir Isaac Newton in 1680, which states: "For every action there exists an equal and opposite reaction which tends to oppose the original action."

THRUST. In jet-propelled powerplants, the reactive force exerted in pounds of pressure by heated air and combustion gases directly on the structure of the powerplant.

THRUST AUGMENTOR RING. A venturi tube superimposed on the jet exit orifice to increase the velocity of the atmospheric air immediately surrounding the orifice up to the point where it equals the velocity of the jetted combustion gases; turbulence

FIGURE 165. Jet Engine Thrustmeter Which Computes Gross Thrust From Tail Pipe and Ambient Pressures.

in the immediate region of the jet orifice is effectively reduced in this manner.

THRUST COMPUTATION. The mass of air utilized is multiplied by the change of velocity of this air mass. In other words, thrust is equal to the mass of the jet discharge per second multiplied by the jet velocity relative to the aircraft; from 0 to 100° F., there is an approximate change of 0.25 percent in thrust per 1 percent temperature change.

THRUST, CONVERSION TO HORSEPOWER UNITS. Jet-power-plant output in terms of thrust can be converted into horsepower ratings, under specific conditions, by multiplying the true air speed by the net thrust and dividing the product by 375.

TORQUE. The turning moment developed by a rotating body and acting in a direction opposite to that of the original rotation.

TURBOFAN. A device with a bladed rotor, actuated by a secondary jet stream; it is an auxiliary source of power and supplements the thrust developed at take-off.

TURBOJET POWERPLANT. A gas turbine and compressor combination in which atmospheric air is compressed, mixed with a hydrocarbon fuel, and burned; the resulting heated gases are directed against the turbine blading prior to being ejected through a rear jet orifice where they generate the reactive force which impels the aircraft forward.

ULTIMATE STRENGTH. The maximum stress exerted on a material at rupture, divided by the original cross-section of the material.

VARIABLE-DISCHARGE TURBINE. Frequently referred to as "VDT." A nozzle of variable discharge characteristics, mounted on a large reciprocating powerplant to provide jet thrust; it increases the power 15 percent; back pressure on the turbine unit is obtained by control of the exhaust nozzle area.

VOLUTE. A diffuser of helical or spiral outline, the purpose of which is to collect the air whirled off the impeller blades of a centrifugal compressor.

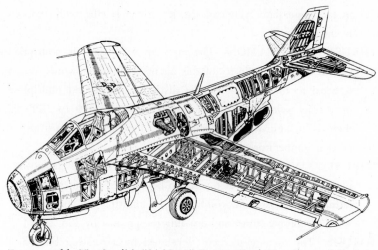

FIGURE 166. The Swedish "SAAB-29" De Havilland-Ghost-Powered Turbojet
Fighter, the "Flying Barrel."

WING LOADING. The gross weight of an airplane, fully loaded,
divided by the area of the supporting surfaces; the area includes
the ailerons and wing flaps, but not the horizontal stabilizer and
elevators.

YIELD POINT. The value of stress at which a pronounced deforma-
tion or deflection of a ductile specimen occurs without an increase
in the applied load.

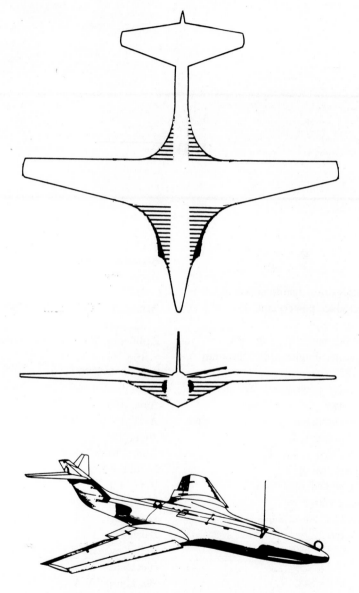

FIGURE 167. Evolution of Convair's Turbojet-Powered Hydroski or Skate-type
Flying Boat, the "Sea Dart." (XF2Y-1)

INDEX